Alice Geer Kelsey

STORIES
of YESTERDAY
and TODAY
for JUNIORS

STORIES
of YESTERDAY
and TODAY
for JUNIORS

Alice Geer Kelsey

ABINGDON PRESS

New York
Nashville

STORIES OF YESTERDAY AND TODAY FOR JUNIORS

Library of Congress Catalog Card Number: 61-5194

SET UP, PRINTED, AND BOUND BY THE
PARTHENON PRESS, AT NASHVILLE,
TENNESSEE, UNITED STATES OF AMERICA

Acknowledgments

Appreciation is here expressed to the editors and publishers of periodicals who have graciously permitted the use of the following stories:

To the American National Red Cross for "Kirk Goes to Market" published as "A Gift for Mother" in the *American Junior Red Cross News*.

To The Brethren Press for "What We Owe Mary Jones," "The Second-Class Rascal," "Owls and Shadows," "The Book from the Street," "Woodpile and Pickle Jar," "On the Barge Canal," "Captain Fuchida," "Bayanihan," "Why the Thumb Stands Alone," and "Bimbo—Hero" in *Journeys*.

To Church World Service for "When Selim Smiled" circulated as "The Turning Point" during the 1959 campaign for One Great Hour of Sharing.

To Longmans, Green and Company for "The Discontented Camanchile Tree" told in the story *Tino and the Typhoon*.

To The Methodist Publishing House for "Cheechako Jim," "The Man Who Came to Die," "Crystal Cave," "Jasvant's Vacation," "Jacob Earns His Salt," and "On the Roof of the World" in *Trails for Juniors*.

To the Philippine Federation of Christian Churches for "A New Name," "New Sharing," "The Church Everybody Built," and "Lola's Song" from Daily Vacation Bible School manuals.

To the Pilgrim Press for "Small Things that Have No Words," "I Can See," and "The Boy Who Mixed His Flags" from *Children's Religion*.

To the Pulpit Digest Publishing Company for "Too Much Dark," "Only the Stars and the Sea Gulls," "When Ben Franklin Stooped," "The Pima Girl," "A Boy and a Bee," "The Ten-Dinar Bath," and "The Spiders' Christmas Eve" from *Pulpit Digest*.

Contents

III Yesterday's Boys and Girls

IV Folk Tales of Yesterday

V The Bible in Today's World

I

Today's Children—Here

Cheechako Jim

"So long, Cheechako! See you tomorrow!" This greeting came from a boy entering the westbound yellow school bus as Jim Mills and his new Indian friend, Pete Owl, were climbing onto the eastbound school bus. A third bus waited by the big modern school in Fairbanks, Alaska. This one was olive drab in color, with *U. S. Army* printed on it.

"So long, Cheechako!" shouted a schoolboy climbing into the bus for army children.

When Jim and Pete were seated side by side Jim asked, "Why do they call you that funny name? Is it Indian for Pete?"

The Indian boy laughed. "They call *you* cheechako!"

"Me? Why?"

"Cheechako is name from gold-rush days. You know who sourdough is?"

"Sure! A tough miner who knew his way around."

"Cheechako was sourdough's name for newcomer who did not know his way around," explained Pete. "I think tenderfoot is the word they use outside. Alaskans still call newcomers cheechako."

"Oh!" Jim was quiet for three blocks before he asked, "How long do I stay a cheechako? We've been in Alaska two months already with Dad's construction company."

"Usually person is cheechako a year or more. Some learn Alaska ways fast. But some always cheechako."

11

"But what do I do that isn't Alaskan?" Jim looked down at his blue jeans and plaid flannel shirt. They were just like Pete's —or would be when he had worn them longer. He felt the small Alaska flag pinned to his shirt pocket, a blue flag with eight gold stars standing for the Great Dipper and the North Star. "I feel Alaskan."

"Well!" Pete was polite. He could think of so many ways that Jim showed he was new. "You call Colorado 'home' instead of 'outside.' In school today you told about seeing caribou in the 'fields.' We say 'tundra.' On Scout hike you tried to dig deep where there was permafrost—too hard for digging."

Then Pete changed to a pleasanter subject. "When you come see my puppies again? Time to break them to harness. Time to teach them to drag chunk of wood so they will drag dog sled when they are big. You come help me."

Mention of those furry, friendly Malemute puppies was enough to make any cheechako forget his troubles. The Indian village was so far away that Jim had been to Pete's house only once. He had liked the friendly Indian family, working so hard to lay in the winter's salmon supply—smoked for themselves, dried for their dogs.

"I'll ask Dad to take me after church Sunday," promised Jim. "How's Smokey? She's my favorite."

"Smokey strongest in litter. She jump over fence of puppy yard twice. I must build higher fence. She too young to be staked and chained like big dogs. Should build fence today, but can't. Must help my father tend fish wheel."

"I can help build a higher fence." Jim knew he was no chee-chako when it came to building. "But here's my stop. So long!"

There were calls of "So long, Cheechako!" as Jim left the bus. He tried not to mind. It was not the Indian boys, the real old-timers, who used the nickname. Neither was it the boys whose grandfathers had been the early prospectors, the sourdoughs. It was the boys who were cheechakos themselves not so long ago.

12

His school was full of near-cheechakos. Their fathers had come from "outside" as aviators, builders, farmers, miners, mechanics, salesmen, government employees.

Jim stood in front of his small green-shingled, flower-banked house waving good-by. His mind followed his Indian friend who would ride a few miles more, then hike a long trail through low trees and bushes to his log home on the banks of the wide, brown Tanana River. Then, Jim knew, Pete would go out on the river with his father in their unpainted rowboat with its sputtering outboard motor to collect the salmon that the great wooden fish wheel had caught as it turned endlessly with the flow of the river.

Jim's new house in its well-watered, green lawn looked dull compared to Pete's log cabin on the banks of the Tanana River. Jim walked through empty rooms. Dad was out where his dredges and bulldozers were at work. There was a note from his mother: "I have taken Susan to Mary Lee's birthday party. I am staying to help Mrs. Lee."

Jim made the usual raid on the refrigerator and cooky jar. He turned on the radio for company while he ate. *Tundra Topics* was on the air. Even though he had said "field" in school today, Jim really knew the meaning of "tundra"—miles of treeless, mucky soil with low growth of blueberries, cranberries, reindeer moss, Labrador tea, dwarf willow, and coarse grass. *Tundra Topics* was a cozy program for people who lived far apart. The program carried messages from person to person as well as news of neighbors. Dick Smith wanted his wife to meet him at the airstrip when the bush pilot brought him in at seven o'clock that evening. Henry Johnson was driving to Palmer and would take anyone who wanted to share expenses of gasoline. The women of the United Church were holding a bake sale tomorrow.

Jim soon had enough of the family chat of *Tundra Topics*. As he had his hand on the knob to turn off the radio, an item caught his ear: "Bob Wright reports seeing wolf on the banks of the Tanana River near Beaver Creek."

"That's close to Pete Owl's house!" Jim thought of the Malemute puppies. "That fence would not keep a wolf out! All the old dogs are staked out. They would be helpless too! I wish Pete Owl's family had a radio!"

A minute later there was another bit of news: "Dave Bull reports seeing wolf tracks on the sandbar of Tanana River near the mouth of Bear Creek."

"That's on the other side of Pete Owl's house!" Jim turned off the radio so he could think. He glanced at the telephone but knew there was none in the Owl home. His mother was away with the car and she would not feel she should leave Mrs. Lee alone with that crowd of six-year-olds. His Dad would feel the same about leaving the construction job he was supervising even if Jim could get him by phone. If anyone was going to the puppies' rescue, it would have to be Jim himself.

He ate one more cooky as he scribbled a note to his mother: "Have gone to Pete Owl's house. Important!!" Jim did not have time to think of problems until he was pedaling away at top speed on his new bicycle. The doubts crowded his mind.

Would he know on which trail to turn off the road? If he found the right trail, did it fork so he might take a wrong turn? What if all Pete's family were out tending their fish traps? If he had to wait to give his warning, it would be dark for the ride home.

Then he had the worst fear of all. He was going straight into the territory where the wolf had been reported. Suppose he met it on the trail? Jim stopped beside a clump of willows to cut a long switch. He had heard that Indians confused wolves and held them at bay by swishing a long willow switch. It seemed slim protection, but an Indian should know.

Jim pedaled past several paths that did not seem like the one where Pete Owl had turned from the road when Jim visited his home. He hid his bicycle in the bushes beside a trail that seemed familiar.

Willow switch in hand, Jim stepped softly. He peered from side to side into underbrush. He saw marks in the trail and hoped they were made by a big dog—not by a hungry wolf.

He heard the fast-flowing Tanana River before he could see it. He heard something else that was not good—the excited barking of dogs. One sharp puppy voice yipped and whimpered like an obligato to the lower barking of the big dogs. Jim ran over the rough trail, slippery with fallen leaves. It sounded like Smokey's yipping. The little dog was plainly in trouble. The big dogs were staked too far away to help.

Jim looked at the footprints in the trail. He slapped his own shaking legs with a stern warning, "Don't be cheechakos! Be sourdoughs!" He cut the air with his willow switch in a steady circle. He whistled a brave medley of tunes. And in the depths of his heart was a prayer: "O God, make me brave! Help me do the right thing!"

Coming into the clearing, he snapped the willow switch and looked toward the dogs. Each big dog was chained beside its own small wooden house. They did not seem frightened—just excited. Seeing Jim with his long whip, they barked harder than ever and pulled at their chains.

Jim took a few hurried steps toward the puppy pen. Then he dropped his switch. "Smokey!" he called. "I'm coming!"

Jim knelt beside the puppy, wedged between boards of her fence. "That's what you get for trying to climb out of your yard! Easy now, Smokey!" Gently Jim pulled posts apart. Gently he pushed Smokey's head back. The puppy was free. She shook her furry head. Whimpering, she licked Jim's hand.

Then Jim remembered why he had come. The puppies and other dogs were not in danger now, but night was fast coming when that wolf could prowl unseen. Looking at the low rail around the puppy yard, Jim knew that the long-legged wolf would not need to "huff and puff" to get inside.

"Good-by, Smokey!" Jim hugged the puppy before putting her

15

back in the pen with her brothers and sisters. "I'll have to find Pete or his family."

There was nobody in the two-room log cabin under the cottonwood trees—nor at the rocks where the Indians cleaned salmon —nor at the smokehouse where salmon were being cured in the smoke of burning black alder branches—nor at the racks where strips of salmon hung to dry. There was nobody near the little log house on posts, the cache where supplies were stored. There was nobody working in the small garden.

Jim walked the few steps to the edge of the Tanana River. He heard the skipping putt-putt of an outboard motor. He saw Pete and all his family coming up the broad, brown river.

Pete was first to leap out on the muddy bank. "Jim! How you come here!"

"I heard something bad over the radio. You ought to know. So I came." Then Jim gave his warning. The Indian family listened gravely.

"Thank you!" said Pete's father. "Bear Creek and Beaver Creek very near. We will be ready for wolf. By dark, the dogs will have safe home. And we will be watching."

"But Jim!" Pete was gazing at his friend. "Weren't you afraid? You might have met wolf—alone!"

Pete was a good listener. Jim told more than he intended to say about being terribly afraid but going on just the same. "But I must go now."

"I go with you to road," said Pete. Jim's heart was glad with the puppy thanks of Smokey and with the quiet Indian thanks of Pete's father, but Pete's schoolboy thanks were best of all. When Jim picked up his bicycle and stood ready to mount it for the ride home, "Pete's grin was wide. "So long, *Sourdough!*" he said. "See you tomorrow!"

(This story is fiction. However, I saw its background details during a visit to Alaska in 1958.)

16

"Too Much Dark"

Susan, the baby sitter, tiptoed down the stairs. The four-year old twins Davey and Donny were asleep—she hoped. The bigger children, Sharon and Keith, had begged for their last story and their last drink of water—she hoped. They were satisfied at last that the outdoor noises were nothing but rain and the branches of trees beating in the heavy wind. The night lamp in the upstairs hall shed friendly light through the open doors of the bedrooms where the children were supposed to be settled for the night.

Susan curled up in an easy chair near the best lamp in the living room. She opened her history book to the chapter she must read before she could watch television. She listened to the whistling of the wind and the pounding of the rain. All was quiet upstairs as Susan studied her homework. But the noises outside grew louder.

Suddenly Susan's reading lamp flickered. Then it blinked out. The hall was dark. The night light upstairs was out. The house was in total darkness. Through the window Susan could see the street lights were out. All the neighbors' houses were dark.

"No more home work!" was Susan's first thought. Then, "What if the children need something? I haven't a flashlight, or a candle, or even a match! I don't know this house well enough to feel my way around in the dark! Oh, I hope the children are asleep—and that they stay asleep!"

Then she heard sounds upstairs, sounds of bare feet stepping carefully in the darkness. She heard the bump-bump-bump of a small person sliding down the stairs. From the hall at the foot of the stairs came a sob and a solemn voice.

"There's too much dark!" wailed Davey. *"There's too much dark!"*

Susan groped toward the voice to comfort the four-year-old.

17

She hoped Donny was sleeping. She heard more footsteps upstairs and the voices of the older children whispering together. Then, to her surprise, Susan saw a flicker of light. Sharon and Keith filed down the stairs, each shielding the flame of a candle.

"We know where Mother keeps candles and matches for emergencies," explained Keith.

"We know where there are more candles down here," added Sharon. The two children went into the dining room and lighted the four candles on the buffet. Then they went into the living room and lighted the two candles on the mantel over the fireplace. They brought out a box of stubby candle ends from a storage closet in the kitchen. "Just in case you need more," Sharon explained.

With the light, Davey stopped crying. Susan picked him up. They all paraded up the stairs again. Davey snuggled cozily in his bed beside his sleeping twin. He knew the candle was burning in the upstairs hall where there had been "too muck dark" a few minutes before.

Susan thanked Sharon and Keith and went downstairs to finish her homework by candlelight. It was not long before repairmen found the broken cable. The regular lights had replaced the candles by the time the children's father and mother came home.

Mother asked the usual question: "Did anything happen?" She knew how many things could happen when a baby sitter was left with four children.

Susan laughed. "In the words of Davey, we had 'too much dark' for a while. All the electric power was off for about half an hour."

"What did the children do?" asked their mother.

"Well, Donny slept and Davey cried," said Susan.

"Just what I'd expect of four-year-olds," said Mother.

"And I just sat because I didn't know what to do," confessed Susan. "But Sharon and Keith did something about 'too much

18

dark.' They found candles and lighted them and lighted some for me too."

"Just what I'd expect of Sharon and Keith," said their father. "Here's hoping they always have sense enough to do something about it when they find 'too much dark' in this old world of ours."

(Source: A personal illustration in an address by Dr. Arthur S. Flemming.)

Only the Stars and the Sea Gulls

You could always count on Harry to do the right thing—when someone was watching. He never threw erasers in school—when the teacher was looking. He never let the air out of the other fellow's bicycle tires—unless he was sure they could not guess who did it.

You could always count on Harry to do good work—when it showed. His room was always tidy—unless you peeked in the bureau drawers or under the bed. His school papers had good marks—at least the ones he brought home.

One summer Harry's Uncle Jack, who was an aviator, came for a visit. At first he thought Harry was wonderful. Then he began to have surprises. There was the time, for instance, that Harry and Uncle Jack were painting the canoe before a camping trip. First they sandpapered it all over to smooth out any rough spots. Then they patched the breaks and the weak spots. Then they sandpapered again, Uncle Jack working on one side of the canoe and Harry on the other.

"Now we're ready for the paint on the outside and the varnish on the inside," said Harry. He stretched to get the bending-over kinks out of his back.

Uncle Jack ran his hands over Harry's side of the canoe. He

19

nodded that all was smooth and ready till he came to the places just under the gunwales.

"What's this?" Uncle Jack scraped off a lump of chewing gum, a flake of loose varnish, and a splinter of wood. "There's another half hour's work getting your side ready."

"But who's going to look under the gunwales?" asked Harry. "I've done a good job where it shows."

Uncle Jack just stood and looked at Harry. "So *that's* your story! That explains a lot of things!"

Harry squirmed. He thought Uncle Jack would say a lot more. Instead, his uncle changed the subject suddenly. "Some day I'll take you for a plane ride."

Of course that was all right with Jack. At last the day for the plane ride came. Harry had thought of plenty of places he would like to see from the air, but Uncle Jack had just one idea.

"We are going to fly over New York Harbor," he announced. "Over the Statue of Liberty."

"I've seen that lots of times," Harry hinted. "I've been there by ferry boat. I've climbed way up to the balcony that runs around the head." But the Statue of Liberty was what Uncle Jack had decided Harry should see from the air.

On the way to the airport Uncle Jack talked about Frédéric Auguste Bartholdi, the French sculptor who made the statue in 1886. "It took a great man to dream a statue which would hold such meaning for generation after generation of people entering New York Harbor. It took a skilled sculptor to make such a gigantic figure and keep it in beautiful proportions. It took a careful workman to get every detail correct."

"Yeah," agreed Harry who had heard all this before.

"You may have my field glasses to look down at the top of the statue when we fly over it," said Uncle Jack. "Remember that in 1886 Bartholdi never dreamed people would be flying over his statue. In those days flying machines were just something to joke about. Bartholdi never expected anything but the stars and the sea gulls to look down on his statue, which would rise higher than the decks of ships in the harbor."

"I'll bet he didn't bother much with the carving on the top of the statue," laughed Harry, "It's a good joke on the old boy to fly over it and look down on the part he thought wouldn't show."

Uncle Jack did not answer. He was busy tuning up his plane for the flight.

Soon they were up in the air, soaring over New York Harbor. The busy tugboats looked as though they came from a toy store. The low-lying freighters looked as though boys had made them from soapboxes. The sea gulls seemed like mosquitoes swooping about.

Harry remembered to use his field glasses when they flew over the Statue of Liberty. He grinned at the trick they were playing on the famous sculptor of long ago, spying on what he thought would be out of sight.

The plane circled several times. Harry had a long clear look at the statue. His grin faded. Uncle Jack smiled as he watched his nephew's face in the mirror over the controls. He knew what the boy was seeing. Every hair on the top of the curly head of the Statue of Liberty was as carefully carved as though Frédéric Auguste Bartholdi, at work in 1886, had known that airplanes would someday be carrying people with field glasses over the top of his statue. The great artist had done every bit of his work well—even the parts that he thought only the stars and the seagulls would ever see.

"The Man Who Came to Die"

"This is where I'm goin' to be in the Easter play!" Grandly Lindy waved a hand toward the littered vacant lot between tenement houses in a crowded part of New York City. The children looked at the trampled dirt strewn with paper bags, broken glass, worn-out shoes, and orange rinds. They laughed. They were not Lindy's friends. She came from another block.

Lindy continued, "Our Easter play is 'The Man Who Came to Die.' " She rolled dark eyes from child to child, hoping they were impressed.

"Oh yeah!" Maria did not miss a skip of her jump rope. "That's just a vacant lot. Easter is in churches."

"Not *this* Easter!" Lindy, small brown hands on her hips, stood ready to defy the whole block if necessary. "We're goin' to build the stage smack up against that board fence."

"Who's we?" Frankie looked up from his game of marbles.

"East Harlem Protestant Parish," said Lindy.

"I heard kids has fun in your church," the boy said wistfully. "All week. Not just preachin' on Sundays."

"That's right," agreed Lindy. "Hikes an' clubs an' choir. They send us to camp summers. An' now we got this Easter Passion Play—an' I'm in it."

"All the kids in your parish in this play?" a hopscotch player asked the question Lindy had been waiting for.

"No—just me an' Dotty an' Victoria. They're both big kids— junior high."

It was exciting enough to be in the Easter Passion Play. To be the only child in it was too much for Lindy. The more she thought about it, the grander grew her manner. The only reason that her friends put up with her chin-in-the-air ways was that everyone was thinking about the play.

Every member of the three small churches of the East Harlem Protestant parish was busy. Women dyed muslin and sewed robes of different colors for the choir and the players. They dyed cheesecloth to make a backdrop. Men and boys measured and sawed lumber for the stage that must be set up quickly just before the play on Good Friday. Others planned the lighting, figuring where to place the colored floodlights. Band, choir, and players practiced and rehearsed.

With each day Lindy felt more important. Her friends wondered why they had ever liked her. She used to be fun, but now she strutted about with her head held high. The young women who directed the play wondered why they had chosen Lindy out of all the delightful children of the three churches of the Parish. She had become so independent and pouty. She would announce "I'm too tired!" when the chorus had to stand longer than she liked. Or she would say, "I'm goin' home now" when she wanted to go to the candy store on the corner. She would whisper and giggle in the serious places of the play and sulk if anyone reproved her.

As the play took shape and seemed real living, however, Lindy began to change. Day after day, when the chorus asked about Jesus, "Who is he?" she would hear what the other players said about him before she spoke her lines, "Some big men pushed me down when I came to see him. He picked me up and talked to me." She began to feel that the real Jesus had given her a hand when other folks were mean to her. The play began to fit the stories she knew about Jesus. Day after day, when they rehearsed the Palm Sunday scene, Lindy stepped up to the minister who acted the part of Jesus and asked him, "Where are you going?" Then the Jesus of the play put his arm around her shoulder and walked across the stage with her. That could not happen often to a girl without her wanting to do her best in the play. Lindy's chin began to come down where it used to be.

By Maundy Thursday, the play was ready—band, choir, costumes, and all. But the vacant lot was just as messy as ever. Scraps and string, old newspapers, stray mittens, broken toys, torn comic books, balls that had been chewed by dogs, covered it. It was a long way, without elevators, from upstairs apartments to trash cans by ground floor doors. It was easier to toss things by what was jokingly called "air express." The lot was far from ready for the Easter play, but the people of the Parish were calm. They knew the plan for Maundy Thursday.

When the doors of Public School 121 opened after classes on that Thursday, there was a dash toward the vacant lot. The boys of the little churches of the East Harlm Protestant Parish were like balls shot from cannon. Boys from junior high and senior high soon joined them. A few girls came, including Lindy.

Rubbish began to fly. Most of it went into piles to be carted away by a city truck. Some children took time out to make collections. Lulu gathered popsicle sticks to bleach for weaving mats. Pablo collected bottle caps, just because it is good for a boy to have a collection to jingle in his pocket. Sam collected pictures from the sports pages of newspapers—especially pictures of Negro athletes who made him proud he was their color. Trash piles grew bigger by the minute. Dozens of boys and girls can make quick work of a clean-up job when their hearts are in it. By supper time the lot was bare and clean except for the piles of trash for the city truck.

Early next morning, men and boys were on the lot to build the stage against the high wooden fence at the back. Some set up spotlights in a room across the street and floodlights on the lot. Others struggled with the amplifier. Others tacked the dyed cheesecloth against the fence. Everything was ready for the play.

When evening came, Lindy slipped on her green muslin gown made in the style of Bible days. Her mother brushed and braided her black hair till not a kink was out of control. With Dotty and Victoria she joined the men and women of the chorus, standing in the shadows at either side of the stage—those in blue on one side, those in deep red on the other. Even Lindy was too excited to whisper or talk as they watched the audience fill the lot.

First came the the people of the three little churches. When the band struck up a spiritual, crowds came to see what was happening. The lot filled. The audience spread onto the sidewalk—into the street. Windows of tenement houses opened and heads appeared. Lindy nudged Dotty and pointed at boys standing on roofs. Victoria nudged Lindy and pointed at a man clinging to a telephone pole. Lindy recognized children she knew in the audience and felt sorry for them. They had not been chosen to play the child of the Easter play.

The French horn sounded the opening notes of the spiritual "Go Tell It on the Mountain." Lights flooded the stage. The green of Lindy's straight little gown mingled with the blue and deep red of the choir as they sang their way to the platform.

The narrator's voice spoke the words that Lindy knew by heart: "This is a story of a man who was born a long time ago. People called him Jesus. He lived a strange life, and there are people even today who find it difficult to believe the stories about his life. But we believe in Jesus, and we believe you will be interested in knowing about him."

Lindy knew what would come next—the voice of a man from the chorus shouting, "What's his story?" Then she knew the play was on its way. Its seven scenes would answer the man's question. They would tell that big crowd of listening people the story of "the man who came to die."

With lights beamed on the stage, Lindy could not see the faces below her in the lot or above her in windows and on roofs. But she knew who was there. The girls in her Sunday-school class—Ada, Carol, Lulu, and Diana. The children from her block—Pedro, Sam, Carmencita, and Rosie. Children from her room at school—Laura, Harry, Domingo, and Maria. In a minute she would be speaking as the only child in the play. She would be speaking for all her friends. Her part suddenly seemed bigger than herself—much bigger.

The choir was answering the man who asked for Jesus' story. They sang, "He called men—to follow *him*—to the Kingdom." It was Lindy's turn now.

She stepped forward and held out her arms. She must speak

clearly for all her friends on the lot and in the windows. "Some big man pushed me down when I came to see him. He picked me up and talked to me." Lindy stepped back into the chorus as they chanted, "There's love in him."

Lindy's big part came in the third scene, the Palm Sunday story. By this time Lindy had stopped thinking how important she was to the play. Now she was thinking how important all children were to Jesus. She joined the chorus chanting, "Hosanna! Hosanna! To the new King!" The choir surged onto the stage, Lindy's small green gown mingling with the red and the blue, singing, "Here comes Jesus riding on a donkey!" She could see him at the end of the procession as they lined the stage and made a road for him to pass. "Hosanna! Hosanna! KING—JESUS!" The man who played the part of Jesus walked into the light. He passed in front of the chorus who cheered him. It was time for Lindy to speak for all the children who loved Jesus.

Lindy stepped from the chorus. "Where are you going?" she asked the man who played the part of Jesus. He stopped and looked at her. There was friendship in his face as he bent toward the child. He made her feel Jesus' love, not just for her but for all children. He put his arm around her shoulder and they walked off together. The light that shone on Lindy's face was not all from the spotlight.

Slowly the narrator answered the question the child had asked. His voice was low and solemn, but it could be heard on the rooftops. "He's going to die!"

Lindy was back in the choir to sing in the scenes showing the Last Supper and the Crucifixion. There was a choke in her voice when the chorus chanted, "See his cross, so heavy; his head bent—so low." To think that he had borne all that for her and for her friends out there in the audience and for all children everywhere. Then the lights showed him standing, arms outstretched against the black shadow of the cross.

Lindy was glad when the Easter scene began. She could feel

happiness going over the big audience when two persons Jesus had helped were shown rejoicing that he had risen from his tomb.

"It's like—like the rain stopping, and the sun shining again! Like a song you got to shout! He's alive—Jesus is alive!"

"We got to tell. Come on! We got to tell somebody quick!"

Lindy was glad she was part of the choir who did the telling in a loud, glad burst of song that could be heard from the Harlem River to Third Avenue.

> Up from the grave He arose
> With a mighty triumph o'er His foes.
>
> . . . . . .
> He arose! He arose!
> Hallelujah! Christ arose!

Lindy knew she was singing for happy Christian children everywhere.

(The quotations are used by permission of the East Harlem Protestant Parish and the authors of "The Man Who Came to Die.")

"Small Things That Have No Words"

Christopher sat on the doorstep of his grandparents' old-fashioned white house. He was saying good-by to the big yard that ran back and back through garden and tall trees to the Ausable River. He was saying good-by to all the small things that swam and fluttered and ran.

Through the open window Christopher heard Grandfather making up songs at the piano. That reminded him that he must say good-by to Grandfather and Grandmother too. But he was not worrying about them. They could tell their needs to the doctor, the grocer, the carpenter, the plumber, and all the folks who made life comfortable. If they needed something their village friends could not do for them, they could ask God for help.

It was different with the small things of the grass, the trees, the garden, and the river. It was hard to say good-by to them. They seemed so little and unprotected. They had no way of asking for help. Christopher did wish there was someone to take care of them after he had gone back to the city!

"Come back, Muffins!" Christopher jumped up from the doorstep and caught the black and white kitten just before she wandered into the road. She rubbed against his cheek, purring as he scolded, "You must learn to stay out of the road. Tomorrow I won't be here to run after you. When Grandmother is working in the kitchen and Grandfather is making up songs at the piano, who will look after you?"

Carrying Muffins, Christopher tiptoed to the stone under the oak tree where he had laid the breakfast prune pits. All were gone but two. His friend the chipmunk was scampering back to carry those two away. Christopher watched her pick them up, one in each stretchy cheek, and scurry off toward the secret place where she hid food for winter.

Next Christopher heard an unsteady flapping of wings. He saw a young robin in awkward flight from low bush to ground. He held Muffins tight when he felt the kitten stiffen and try her claws.

"No, Muffins!" Christopher scolded her. "You are not going to touch that baby bird. We are going to stay right here to keep other cats away till she is off the ground."

After the young robin fluttered back into a bush, Christopher · walked through the garden and the fields to the river. He was saying good-by to the small things he had grown to love: butterflies hovering over the flower beds . . . the toad hunting insects in the tomato patch . . . the humming bird on spinning wings feeding in the columbine blossoms . . . the shiny turtle sunning itself on a log in the river . . . the green frog that dove from the bank with a splash . . . the lucky-bugs and water spiders darting and skimming over the water's surface . . . the fish, no longer than Christopher's finger, swimming close together as though they needed company. He must say good-by to all these small things.

"Christopher!" mother called from the house. "Time to get ready to go!"

Mother did not understand that Christopher was very busy getting ready to go home. The small things outdoors seemed much more important to him than a clean suit and brushed hair. But he would hurry back to the house and be quick, to satisfy Mother's ideas of being clean for travel. Then there might be time to talk with Grandfather about the little animals and birds and fish that must be left behind. Grandfather always had good ideas.

Christopher was out of breath from running when he stood beside Grandfather at the piano. The music stopped and Grandfather looked up with his what-can-I-do-for-you smile.

"I'm worried about the chipmunk and the baby robin and all the small things that live in the garden and the trees and the river," said Christopher.

"You mean bees and lizards and rabbits and woodpeckers?" Grandfather was always quick to understand.

"And moths and field mice and snails," Christopher added "I've sort of watched out for them while I'm here. I wish there was some way I could feel safe about them after I go way. They're all so little. And they can't talk. They need someone bigger who knows what they need."

"They do have Someone Bigger who understands what they need," said Grandfather. "Your part can be reminding him that you care too. Let me teach you a short prayer poem that came to me once on a Christmas card:

'Dear Father, hear and bless
Thy beasts and singing birds,

29

> And guard with tenderness
> Small things that have no words.'"

"I could learn it faster if there was a tune," said Christopher.

"By the time you are cleaned up for your trip, I'll have a tune for your 'small things that have no words,'" Grandfather promised.

Christopher saw the thinking-music look on Grandfather's face. He tiptoed from the room. While he was bathing, he listened as well as he could over the splashing. At first there was silence in the living room where Grandfather sat at his piano. Then the music began—soft and slow. So Christopher knew that Grandfather would keep his promise.

Scrubbed and starchy neat, Christopher stood again beside the piano. Grandfather sang the new song once—twice. Then Christopher and Grandfather sang it together:

Dear Fa-ther, hear and bless Thy beasts and sing-ing birds, And guard with ten-der-ness Small things that have no words. A - men.

Christopher was singing it as he climbed into the car and rode back toward the city. He was not worrying any more. He and God were partners now in caring for the "small things that have no words."

(The music is copyright by H. Gifford Bull and published by the Ulysses Press, Keeseville, New York. Used by permission of Helen Bull. The author of the words of the song is unknown.)

II

Today's Children—There

Crystal Cave

At the same time, two pairs of brothers were moving toward the same twisted pine tree. Marking the trail to Crystal Cave, it stood near the road that wound upward from the mile-high Philippine city of Baguio toward the green summit of Mount Santo Tomas. Neither pair of brothers knew about the other—yet. But how well they would know each other before the sun set!

The freckle-faced West brothers climbed into a blue-and-yellow jeepney, a jeep-like hired car that carried passengers. They were leaving the gate of Camp John Hay where families of United States Air Force men took vacations from the tropical heat of Clark Field in the lowlands.

At the same time, five miles away, the dark-eyed Gambito brothers climbed down the bamboo ladder from their square mountain house, with its walls and floors of bamboo and its roof of cogon grass.

In the bouncing jeepney, Roger West asked his bigger brother Micky, "Are you *sure* you know the way to Crystal Cave?" Micky reminded him that he went there with the scout troop only six months ago.

Outside their mountain hut five miles away, Tito Gambito asked his bigger brother Tony in the mountain dialect, "Do you think we'll get any guiding jobs today?" Tony reminded him that the big round rice basket was almost empty. They must earn at least a peso to buy more rice.

33

The Gambito brothers were first to reach the twisted pine tree that marked the trail to Crystal Cave. Tito and Tony squatted on their heels, Filipino-fashion. They grasped their unlighted pine torches and watched hopefully for customers. Cars passed them by—a red and green jeepney carrying passengers to a mountain barrio of thatched bamboo houses, a truck with supplies for the men repairing the road toward the summit, a red station wagon full of lowlanders admiring the mountain scenery.

At last a blue-and-yellow jeepney pulled up beside them. Two foreign-looking boys paid the jeepney driver, climbed down the steps, and looked in their direction.

"Americanos!" Tito whispered to Tony.

"Look at their faces. Their eyes are *blue* and their hair is the color of rice straw. They are too big all over."

Tony turned to Roger and Micky and said in his slow and careful English, "Crystal Cave? You need guides? No?"

"No guides for us!" Micky brushed past them.

Roger followed his older brother, asking anxiously, "Are you *sure* we don't need a guide, Micky?"

"Who wants a couple of Igorots for guides!" Micky called over his shoulder.

The way Micky said "Igorots," the name for mountain people, hurt their pride, but the Gambito brothers must earn rice money. They ran beside Micky and Roger.

"To find Crystal Cave is hard," said Tony.

"Not for me!" grunted Micky.

Micky was striding fast but Tony's nimble mountain legs kept up easily. "In Crystal Cave is very dark," said Tony. "Our pine torches give light."

Micky turned his powerful flashlight in Tony's face, then in Tito's face. He laughed to see the boys jump and blink.

In quick anger, Tito raised his pine torch as a club. Tony grabbed his arm.

34

"I don't like them!" Tito muttered in his mountain speech. "I hope they miss the trail! I hope Pedring's bull chases them! I hope they get lost in the cave—forever!"

"They don't like us either," said Tony. "Let's forget them!"

The mountain brothers went back to their place under the twisted pine tree to wait for customers. They could not forget the foreigners who refused to be friendly.

"Someone should teach them manners!" said Tito.

"Not us!" said Tony.

"Why not?" Tito had a sudden idea. "We could give them a good scare—in Crystal Cave!"

Tony turned to his little brother. "How?"

"We could run fast through the jungle. We could be at the cave before they get there by trail. We could hide in the cave and make such scary noises that they would never go near a cave again if they lived to be as old as Mount Santo Tomas."

Tony grinned. "We know the way to the far end of the cave where no trail leads. We can circle through the woods where those foreign boys can't see us from their trail."

They watched the Americanos plodding noisily down the path.

"They walk like carabaos!" said Tito scornfully.

Then Tony and Tito took off through the forest of mountain pines and tropical underbrush. They ran like goats—not like carabaos. They knew the hillside too well to need a trail. Skilled in jungle travel, they beat their way through twining vines, over slippery stream beds, across the steep pasture where Pedring's bull grazed.

When they reached the farther mouth of the Cave they could hear the voices of Roger and Micky shouting far down the trail.

Roger: "Are you sure we turn that way?"

Micky, mimicking: "'Are you sure—are you sure—are you sure!' I'll bet you wish we'd paid those skinny little Igorots to show us the way!"

Grinning at each other, Tito and Tony slid into the mouth of

35

the cave. They were out of hearing now of the shouts of the other boys.

A few steps within the cave Tito and Tony were in darkness. Striking matches, they lighted their pine torches to find their way to a good crevice for hiding. The passage was high enough for a grown person to walk erect if he had a light to help him avoid the stalagmites rising from the floor of the cavern and the icicle-shaped stalactites hanging from its ceiling. There were puddles to avoid also, and slippery rocks, and sudden turns. There might be poisonous snakes so the boys held their burning torches high and stepped with care.

Soon Tony and Tito found a place to hide behind stalagmites and stalactites that met to form a screen. The boys blew out their lights, snuggled tight against the wall of the cave, and tapped each other's lips as a reminder of silence. They waited.

Soon they heard hollow and muffled voices echoing from the other end of the cave's passage. It was easy to tell Micky's big, bold voice from Roger's small, uncertain voice.

Micky: "Well, here we are in Crystal Cave! Who said I couldn't follow a trail?"

Roger: "It looks awfully dark!"

Micky: "Of course it's dark. We came to collect bats. You don't expect to find bats in sunshine, do you? Follow me down this ladder."

Roger: "I wish you'd hold the flashlight so I can see where I'm going."

Micky: "Keep moving. Then you'll stay with the light."

Roger: "I wish we had two flashlights, so I could hold one! Let me carry it."

Micky: "You're too little. You'd fall down and break it."

Roger: "Ouch! I bumped my head. . . Wait for me. . ."

Micky: "Hurry up, slowpoke! . . . Ouch!"

Hiding behind their natural screen, Tito and Tony held their mouths to keep back the snickers. Though they dared not whisper to each other, they both felt a little sorry about Roger's bumped head but more than a little glad about Mickey's.

Tony nudged Tito. Together the boys let out a mournful owl-like "Hoo-oo-oo-oot!" Then they heard:

Roger: "What's that, Mickey?"

Micky: "Some kind of Philippine owl. They don't hurt people, I hope. I'll throw the light high to frighten it."

Roger: "Throw the light low. I can't see to walk."

Micky: "Just feel your way. Don't be a sissy. See how I . . ."

Micky never finished telling Roger what to see. There was a splash that made the mountain boys want to giggle again. There was the sound of breaking glass—a scream from Roger—a groan from Micky.

Roger: "It's too dark—blacker than any dark ever was. What's the matter?"

Micky: "My flashlight. I dropped it when I fell in the puddle. It's gone out. I can't find it."

A few feet away from the Americanos in the darkness, Tony nudged Tito. "Hoo-oo-oot!" moaned and echoed through the cave. Then the mountain boys heard:

Micky: "That owl again. He won't hurt us."

Roger: "I'm not s-s-scared of owls."

Tony whispered in Tito's ear. The mountain boys held their heads close together and opened their mouths. "Woo-oo-oof!" growled and echoed through the cave. "Grr-rr-rr! . . . Hiss-ss-sst! . . . Brr-rr-rrt!" Then Tony put his hands to his lips and gave a piercing whistle that seemed to make the rocks of the cave jiggle. Now they heard action from the boys in the middle of the long, dark passage.

They heard noise as of blind cattle stampeding. There was splashing in puddles, tearing of blue jeans on rocks, screams when heads bumped down-hanging rocks or when toes stumbled over up-poking rocks. Bodies thudded as Roger and Micky collided and fell down. There was silence a minute. Then Tito and Tony heard voices again:

Roger: "Wh-wh-what shall we do?"

Micky. "W-w-wait till someone comes."

Roger: "We'll starve or d-d-die of thirst."

Micky: "Don't be a b-b-baby!"

Roger: "I w-w-wish you'd let those nice Filipino boys show us the way with their p-p-pine torches. Those mountain kids really meant to help us. They knew their way in the cave without a scout leader."

Micky: "Okay, you're right. Pine torches are better than flashlights for caves."

Smiling broadly, Tito started to light his torch. Tony stopped him. He wanted to be sure Micky had learned his lesson. The brothers listened. Once more hollow voices rounded the bends of the black passage of Crystal Cave.

Micky: "I sure was a heel, thinking I was so smart. Those Filipino kids are smarter than I am."

Roger: "Their manners are better than ours, too."

Micky: "If we get out of here alive, I'll hunt 'em up and say I'm sorry. Well, let's get going. It's pitch dark but if we keep moving, we'll get to the opening."

Roger: "Which w-w-way?"

Micky: "I—don't—know! I wish I'd been decent to those boys!"

There were two scratches as Tito and Tony struck matches to light their pine torches. Sparks flickered and sputtered. Torches blazed with a clean yellow light. The mountain boys, sure footed on the uneven ground, hurried toward the Americanos.

"Crystal Cave? You want guides? No?" shouted Tony.

All that Micky and Roger answered was "Yes!" But in that one word was all the relief and all the apology that any words could carry.

"We show you bats," offered Tony as the mountain boys picked their way nimbly over the rocks toward the other pair of brothers. "We walk to end of cave first. We see bats on way back."

Roger asked a question. "Must we pass the animals that make the terrible noises?"

"Like this?" asked Tony. Together the mountain boys let out a series of wild cries. "Woo-oo-oof! Gr—r-rr! Hiss-ss-sst!"

In the light of the pine torches Roger and Micky stared at the boys who were making noises like a jungle on the march. Then Roger gave a surprised giggle. Micky let out a shamed titter. Then all four boys burst into a roar of laughter that echoed through the hollow tunnel of Crystal Cave.

"The loud screech. . ." said Micky. "Teach me how to do that!"

Then as the four friends picked their way by the blaze of the pine torches, there were noises that made the drowsy bats squeak and cling tighter than ever to the crevices of the dark, damp walls.

(This story is fiction, but the boys with the pine torches are real. They piloted us through Crystal Cave with great skill.)

Bayanihan

Pepito sat in the thick shade of the mango tree beside the well that gave clean water for his Philippine village a mile away. He fanned himself with his palm leaf hat and sniffed the sweetness of the fluffy blossoms among the dark green leaves over his head. He wondered how long he must wait for the blossoms to grow into juicy, yellow fruit.

He wondered, also, how long it would take little Celeste to finish pumping her jar of water. He had waited while old Aling Nenet filled her shallow, scalloped-edge washtub and squatted beside it to pound her clothes with her wooden paddle. She was slow because she was old. He had waited while two small brothers named Pedro and Elberto had filled kerosene tins with water and gone off with it sloshing-sloshing from the middle of the carrying pole resting on a shoulder of each boy. They were slow because the long wooden handle of the Liberty Well's pump was heavy for such small boys. Now Celeste was taking too much time. The pump handle was so heavy that she had to jump up with it and then ride down on it with all her weight.

It was comfortable enough under the mango tree, but Pepito's mother had told him to hurry home. "Remember this is the day of the *bayanihan* when men of the village will help your father move our house. They will be thirsty and there will be many of them. One coke apiece is all we can afford to give them. We must have plenty of water for them to drink."

Watching Celeste ride up and down slowly on the long pump handle, he called to her, "What do you think that is? Are you riding or pumping? I want my turn."

Celeste did not answer. It took all of the little girl's breath to keep the pump handle going fast enough to bring up a little trickle of water.

Aling Nenet had an answer for Pepito. She pounded her clothes harder as she shouted to him," Pepito, do you forget the good Filipino custom of *bayanihan?*"

"No, it is because of *bayanihan* that I am in a hurry." Pepito did not move from his comfortable spot in the shade of the mango tree. He fanned himself faster as he answered, "I must get home with this water in time for the *bayanihan* at our house."

Aling Nenet said, "O Pepito! Pepito! You do not understand the real meaning of *bayanihan!*"

A polite Filipino boy cannot contradict an older person, so Pepito merely *thought* the things he wanted to say. "I do know what *bayanihan* means. Aren't all the strong men of our village coming today to help my father lift our house from its posts and carry it half a kilometer down the road? They will walk along singing and laughing with their strong shoulders under the two poles holding the house. My mother will be there with food for them when they have settled our house firmly on its new posts on the land we bought from Ramon Reyes. I guess I do know that *bayanihan* means the neighbors working together when one of them has something too hard to do alone!"

Being polite, Pepito said none of this as he watched little Celeste finally fill her jar. She lifted it to her head with difficulty and walked slowly down the dirt road toward home, balancing it with the touch of the fingers of one hand.

Then Pepito filled his pails quickly. He was strong and could manage the pump easily. He hung his pails on the ends of his carrying pole, stooped till one shoulder was under the pole, then stood erect. He hurried down the road with quick short steps, splashing only a little water as he walked.

He passed between two fields with their small rice seedlings standing straight and green in the muddy water. He overtook Celeste and spoke to her pleasantly. "That was a good *bayanihan* we had in these fields last week when everyone in the village came out to plant Ramon Reyes' rice. It was fun to work together keeping time to Val's guitar."

Then he passed the place where a hole in the road was partly mended. He knew the men of the village would be back working at it together when they had caught up on their farm work after moving the house for his father. He overtook Pedro and Elberto and called to them, "That was a good *bayanihan* we had here. It was fun to work together."

"You didn't think of *bayanihan* when you watched us pump and scolded us for being slow," shouted Pedro.

Suddenly Pepito remembered what Aling Nenet had said. She was right. He had not understood what *bayanihan* meant. It was more than moving a house together, or planting rice together,

41

or making a road together. It was working together, even if you were a boy waiting for your turn at the well.

Pepito turned his head to call over his shoulder to Pedro and Elberto. "Tell me next time you have to go to the well for water. I'll go with you. We'll have a good *bayanihan*."

(Note: The word *bayanihan* (bah-yah'-nee-hahn) can be translated *work-bee*. The English phrase, however, fails to suggest the warmth and laughter and festive air of Filipinos working together.)

"I Can See"

Pilar could hear the birds singing in the bamboo trees over her little thatched hut in a mountain village of the Philippine island of Mindanao, but she could not see the birds. Pilar could feel the wind blowing on her face, but she could not see how it made the coconut palms or banana trees wave their long branches. Pilar could smell the wood smoke from the outdoor fireplace where her mother cooked their meals, but she could not see it puffing up toward the treetops. Pilar could taste the rice her mother heaped on her plate, but she had to grope with her fingers to find it.

Pilar could remember how some things looked. Four years ago, when she was very little, she could see as well as any one of her Manobo tribespeople. But then her eyes began to hurt. Things began to look fuzzy and blurry.

There was no doctor in Pilar's mountains, and there was not enough money to ride the bus to the faraway city to find a doctor. The Manobo hill people were shy about cities anyway. So Pilar's eyes grew dimmer and dimmer. Finally she was known as "the little blind girl." Pilar did not suppose she would ever see anything again. She could just taste, and hear, and smell, and touch, and move about—but never see.

Then great news came to the little Manobo village in the hills. A man from another group of small thatched huts told them, "On the fourth Saturday of every month a doctor comes to our village. He comes in a jeep. He brings nurses and helpers with him. Bring Pilar to see this Doctor Sam. Perhaps he can help her eyes."

"A doctor?" Pilar's father could hardly believe that. "Doctors never come to us. We are too far away. And nobody here is rich enough to pay a doctor or nurse. Why do they come?"

"He is a Christian Filipino doctor," explained the man "He and the other Christians tell about a man named Jesus who healed people because he loved them. They are trying to be like Jesus. They care more about helping people than they care about money."

Pilar listened—and hoped.

"Day after tomorrow is their time to come," said the man.

"We will bring Pilar," promised her father.

When the day came, Pilar's mother led her along the jungle trail to the highway. The girl could hear a monkey chattering in the high coconut palm and the bulbuls singing in the wild papaya trees. She had almost forgotten how monkeys and birds looked. Her mother held back the branches so that Pilar would not be scratched by them. She carried her over the roughest parts of the trail.

Finally they reached the highway where noisy cars whizzed past. There were the loud sounds of trucks or of buses too loaded to stop for two Manobos standing by the side of the road. There was the slow pad-pad of carabao's feet, or the quick scuff-scuff of women walking in their wooden sandals. There was the sudden puff of wind as a passenger car dashed past them.

At last a big wooden bus stopped. Pilar's mother helped her climb on a high step and find a place on a bench of the open bus. The girl liked the breeze in her face as the bus jolted along the highway. She could hear little over the noise of the bus but her nose told her what they were passing. She smelled the smoke of wood fires when they rode through villages, the perfume of flowers by the side of the road, the dampness near the brooks they crossed. Finally the bus stopped at the little jungle village where the Christians from the lowlands came to help sick people. The doctor's jeep was there already.

Doctor Sam looked at Pilar's eyes. He asked many questions. He talked with the nurse. He looked at the little girl's eyes again. Pilar was not afraid, because his voice made her trust him.

"May I take her to the hospital in Davao?" he asked. "There is a doctor there—a Chinese doctor—who knows more about curing eyes than I do."

"But we have no money," said Pilar's mother, "not enough money to pay a Chinese doctor in a big city."

"He is a Christian doctor. He will be happy to help Pilar without pay," said Doctor Sam.

"But the hospital would cost money," said Pilar's mother.

"It is a Christian hospital also," said the doctor. "If people have money, they can pay. If they do not have enough money, the doctors and nurses take care of them just the same. The church people of the Philippines and of America pay for the ones who cannot pay."

"But it's a long way to Davao," objected Pilar's mother. The girl listened—and hoped.

"I will take her in my jeep to my home in Midsayap," offered Doctor Sam. "Friends from there will take her to the hospital in Davao."

Pilar could feel her mother's hand squeezing hers tightly. She heard her mother's voice, "Pilar can go."

The long trip to the city was scary for the blind girl from a non-Christian tribe in the hills. But everyone was good to her. When she reached the big Brokenshire Memorial Hospital, she found the nurses kind, their hands gentle, their laughter happy. The Chinese doctor, too, had a kind voice and gentle hands. Pilar felt sure that helping a blind girl to see was important to him—even a blind Manobo girl from the faraway hills.

In the hospital Pilar learned stories about Jesus who healed people. She began to understand why the nurses and doctors were trying to be like him.

The good Chinese doctor found the right medicine for Pilar's eyes. It was a happy day in the hospital when Pilar said, "I can see!" It was a happy day for the doctors and nurses. It was a very happy day for Pilar. She made a song of it, saying it over and over, "I can see! I can see! I can see!"

(I think of Pilar as a personal friend. We were guests together, Pilar as a long-time guest, in the home of Mr. and Mrs. Guy Thelin, missionaries of the United Church of Christ in the Philippines. At last report, Pilar was happily attending the elementary school of Southern Christian College in Midsayap, living in the home of a church member, and going for visits to her hill village.)

When Selim Smiled

"Tell me about Mount Carmel, Mother!" Kemal, a Christian Arab boy, watched his mother's small stitches as she sewed blue patch on plaid patch on his brown trousers.

"Which story? About the Prophet Elijah on Mount Carmel? The time he proved his God was strongest?" Faride, mother of Kemal, glanced up from her sewing to be sure the fire was burning properly in the outdoor fireplace where rice was steaming in a clay pot.

"Not a Bible story this time," said Kemal. "Tell about Mount Carmel and us—about the house where I was born."

"Our old home was like this in three ways." Faride always began with the good things. "We can still lift up our eyes to

45

purple-gray hills, the Lebanon mountains now. We can still wash our clothes in a stream of living water flowing from the hills into the Mediterranean. And we are again in a village—not a refugee camp such as is home to so many Arabs."

Then Faride was silent, bent over her patching. To see what was different between the old and the new they did not need to look through the door into the small dark room they shared with another refugee family. They did not need to look at the neighborhood cluttered with flimsy houses, too small and too close together.

"Tell about our old home," begged Kemal.

"It was in a walled garden where lilies of every color made the air sweet." The remembering look came into Faride's eyes. "The stone house was big. Three bright rooms with real glass windows and a flat roof of red tile."

Kemal tried to imagine the house. He had been too small to remember that dreadful night when the soldiers of the Israeli army captured their town, and the Arabs fled with nothing but their children and what they could carry in cloth bundles. Listening to his mother, Kemal did not hear footsteps—slow, discouraged footsteps. His mother went on with her remembering —about the bougainvillaea whose purple blossoms covered the front doorway, about the pink-flowered almond trees, about the neighbors who were kind and friendly.

"And when the day's work was done," she said, "I would pick up my baby. That was you, Kemal. Then I would rest under our grapevine waiting for your father to come home from the government office where he worked."

The slow footsteps had stopped beside Kemal and his mother. A voice as weary as the footsteps spoke. "And there was work for a man in those days! A man could support his family!"

They looked up quickly into the sad face of Kemal's father, Selim. They did not need to ask if he had found work that day. He spoke again. "I hate to think how many years it is since we

46

fled from home in 1948. How many days have I worked? The three of us could count them on our fingers!"

"But we must be grateful to those who have kept us alive," Faride said gently. "Don't forget our daily rations from UNRWA.* What would we have done without their beans, rice, oil, salt, and soap? Remember Kemal's school! And there is always a clothing distribution from Church World Service before our clothes get too ragged to patch again."

"Church World Service!" Selim's face suddenly came alive. "That reminds me what I heard today! It might be true! Hasan said Church World Service loaned him money to buy cobbler's tools to start his old trade again. He said loans from Church World Service, without interest, had helped others start earning again."

"You could borrow too, Father!" Kemal was happy at the possibility.

"But you were a government worker," Faride reminded her husband. "No Arab refugee could get such work here."

"I was a farm boy first," said Selim.

"You could not borrow enough to buy a farm!" Faride objected.

"Not a whole farm," Selim agreed. "But what about a few bees?"

"Bees? Could I help with them?" Kemal was ready to begin that very day.

"I will go to Church World Service and find if they will help me." Selim spoke slowly, thinking his plan. "Perhaps they will lend me money to buy a book on beekeeping, then money to buy bees and the hives. The flowers for the bees are on the hillsides."

"I'll go to market to sell honey. And there'll be honey to eat on our bread." The boy planned faster than his father.

* United Nations Relief Works Administration.

47

Kemal felt this was the most important day since the flight from the Mount Carmel country. Though his parents had tried to live their Christian faith, it had been hard to hope month after month, trusting God had a plan for their happiness. Thanks to UNRWA they had not starved. Thanks to Church World Service they had not been too cold, though the wind sometimes blew through their old clothes before new ones came out of the big bales from America. Living on relief was hard for people who wanted to earn their own way.

Because he wanted to be part of any action so important, Kemal begged to go to the Church World Service office with his father. Selim liked company. And he was glad Kemal cared.

There were buses running to Beirut, but walking cost nothing. It was not too long a journey for a man and a boy with new hope to put springs in their feet. They did not mind the white dust from automobiles that whizzed past. They exchanged greetings with men afoot and men on black donkeys.

Finally, their road led down into the beautiful seaside city of Beirut, with its big stone buildings, its endlessly winding streets, its crowds of strangers, its flowering vines and tall cedars, and its great university. Kemal looked longingly at the tram cars that clattered over tracks. But trams were like buses; riding cost a coin. Kemal and his father walked the hilly streets, asking the way to the office of Church World Service.

Kemal did not mind sitting beside his father in the waiting room. Looking at faces, he saw kindness and hope. When it was his father's turn, Kemal followed him to the desk of a man who seemed to have the answers for people's problems.

It did not take Kemal's father long to prove that he really wanted to support his family, and that he had a clear idea how he could do it. The man at the desk knew what to do. Kemal and Selim waited while he rang several numbers on the phone. Sometimes he talked in a strange language. Kemal thought it might be English. Other times he talked in Kemal's language,

Arabic. Kemal understood enough to guess what was going to happen. His eyes grew rounder and wider and brighter as he listened.

At last the man at the desk turned to them. "One of my assistants will be at the door in his jeep in fifteen minutes. He will drive you to see a man who is a master beekeeper. This man will sell you four colonies of bees with the hives and all the equipment you need to start the honey business. My assistant will take you and the bees back to your village by jeep."

Before the man at the desk had finished speaking, Kemal was already looking out the window for the first glimpse of the jeep that would take them on their great adventure. He did not understand how his father could sit so calmly filling out forms and agreeing how the borrowed money would be paid back to Church World Service after enough honey had been sold.

As they sped along in the jeep, Kemal had no eyes for the olive orchards, or flat-roofed houses, or travelers on the dusty white road, or purple-gray mountains in the distance. He saw only what the driver was doing with hands and feet. He heard only the throb and rattle of the jeep. He felt only the wind buffeting his face as the car whizzed along the road.

Even the jeep ride was forgotten when they stopped at the home of the beekeeper. Kemal missed no word as the man explained how to clean the hives, what to do when the bees swarmed, how to take out the honeycomb, how to strain the honey ready for market.

On the ride home Kemal's ears were keyed to a sound far softer than jeep noises. His music was the excited buzzing of four colonies of bees. Their buzzing made background for happy thoughts, for many questions. Could he help care for the bees? Could he go to market to sell honey? Could he help his mother make beeswax candles? Could he sell the extra candles in market?

Turning to ask his father these questions, Kemal learned this was a time too glad for talking. On his father's face was a smile Kemal had never seen. It must have been like the smile his father used to have before 1948 when he came home from work to his wife and baby sitting under the grapevine in his own walled garden. Selim's shoulder's were straight and his chin was held high. It seemed, over the buzzing of the jeep, that Kemal could hear his father humming a tune, a happy tune. Kemal had never heard him do that before.

There was just one question Kemal must ask. "Father, will there be enough beeswax that I can make a special candle—for Christmas?"

There seemed to be Christmas in Selim's smile as he said, "As many Christmas candles as you want, my son!"

(Source: Conversation with William Haddad, General Secretary of Bible Lands Union for Christian Education and member of the Beirut committee administering Church World Service. The father in the story had already repaid his loan. His personal dignity restored by becoming an earner, he had also found evening employment as a teacher.)

Kirk Goes to Market

The big wooden gate in the high wall of the clay-colored bricks clicked shut behind Kirk. Whistling, he walked down the dusty road between two rows of brick walls. He felt he had already accomplished what he had been planning so long.

He was so pleased about it all that he quickly forgot the hurt and lonesome look of his small brother when he had shut the door in Johnny's face with the usual, "Sorry! You're too little."

He did wish for just a minute that he had promised to bring Johnny something from the bazaar. It was tough being only four years old and in a foreign land, with no playmates. Even the black and white puppy had surprised everyone by growing so big and rough that he knocked Johnny down instead of keeping him company.

Soon Kirk forgot Johnny, and remembered with pride the three problems he had solved before he was ready to take this trip alone to the fascinating bazaar in the city of Mashad in Iran.

First, he had found out what his mother wanted for her birthday. When he asked her outright she would say something like, "The best birthday present any mother could have is to know that her children are happy!"

That was not much of an answer. Of course Kirk was happy with a swimming pool, trips on the jeep, his workbench and tools, and his Iranian friends. And there was nothing anyone could do to make Johnny happy. He needed someone to play with, but there was not anyone the right size.

Kirk felt he was smart to have found out what his mother wanted for her birthday. He had been sitting in the room once when Susan's mother was calling on his mother. The two women talked about the turquoise shop in the bazaar.

Kirk learned that turquoise was a lovely blue stone that was mined, as it had been for centuries, near Nishapur, the nearest big town. He learned that every American woman in Iran wanted some turquoise from these world-famous mines.

When Susan's mother said to Kirk's mother, "With your blue eyes, you should always wear turquoise," Kirk knew that turquoise from the Nishapur mines was what he must buy for his mother's birthday.

His second problem was easier—getting money to buy the gift. That meant saving from his allowance for weeks, and adding to it the prize money he earned from his Dad by doing well in the lessons he studied every morning with his mother.

His third problem was really hard—getting permission to go alone to the bazaar. For days he had been trying to prove to his

51

family that he could speak Farsi, the language of Iran, better than either his father or mother. He was sure he knew his way around the bazaar. If he should lose his way, he could call a droshky, give his home address, and ride home in one of the high covered carriages behind a pair of jogging horses wearing tinkling bells.

It was not till the day of her birthday that his mother agreed to let Kirk go alone to the bazaar. He hoped she did not guess why he wanted to go.

He was sorry it was so late, but at least he would not have the problem of hiding the turquoise jewelry. He could give it to her with a hug and a "Happy Birthday" as soon as he came within the street gate on the way home.

Swinging down the road between the high street walls of his Iranian neighbors, Kirk was surprised to find how much longer it was on foot than by jeep. He turned onto the broader street with its four rows of tall trees, then onto the street that led to the huge golden dome and tall minarets of the famous shrine of Imam Riza.

Just before time to turn onto the broad street of the turquoise shop, Kirk heard a familiar sound: "Hee-haw, hee-haw." But it was not the braying of a single donkey. It was the noise of many donkeys.

"The donkey market!" Kirk told himself. "I've always wanted to go there and watch them buy and sell donkeys. But there's never time when I'm with someone else. Now is my chance to go—just for a minute to see what it is like."

So Kirk turned off the street, away from the turquoise shop. He followed the sound of the braying of many donkeys to an open place where men wandered among dozens of gray or white donkeys. The men poked them here and poked them there to see which ones were plumpest and strongest.

A few months ago, Kirk would have been excited to see so many donkeys, but since he had been in Iran he had seen hundreds of patient little donkeys, tripping along through the streets under heavy loads balanced in their saddle bags or saddle frames.

As he turned to walk away, he felt something warm and soft and damp on the back of his neck. He turned around quickly. There, stretching its neck to look him squarely in the eyes, was a white baby donkey. It was the smallest and whitest donkey that Kirk had ever seen. It made a few prancing steps. It twinkled its brown eyes at him. It waggled one long ear forward at him, then the other ear. It pranced again.

"How much?" Kirk asked the price, just out of curiosity, from the owner. But before he knew what was happening, Kirk was bargaining in good Middle Eastern style.

As the barganing went on, just for fun of course, Kirk began to forget why he had the roll of paper money in his pocket. The donkey had such a friendly way of twitching its ears whenever Kirk won a few rials on the price. It seemed to be cheering for Kirk, hoping he would be the next owner.

A crowd of men and boys gathered to watch the bargaining. It was not every day that a fair-skinned American boy came into the donkey market. Why did a boy who could ride in a jeep want a donkey? Americans were always doing queer things!

A few rials at a time, Kirk worked the price down to half the amount he carried in his pocket. He could buy the donkey, though of course he did not intend to, and still have enough money to buy a small gift in the turquoise shop.

"I'll raise the price," said a rough and disagreeable voice, speaking Farsi which Kirk could understand quite well. Kirk turned to see a dirty, bearded man on a skinny white donkey whose head hung down as though life was very hard.

Kirk could not let such a man buy the baby donkey. The boy offered five rials more. The man offered ten. Kirk raised the price again. So did the man. A few rials at a time, Kirk kept raising the price, hoping to outbid the man.

A crowd gathered to see the fun. Kirk had decided to spend every rial in his pocket to save the donkey from such a master. Kirk bid his last rial. The man raised the price again. The donkey's owner looked at Kirk. The boy shook his head and turned away.

"Wait!" the owner called in Farsi. "I can lose a few rials to give the little donkey a good home. You can have him for the price you bid."

With the small donkey nuzzling his arm, Kirk handed the money to its owner. There was a good-by chorus of "Hee-haw, hee-haw," from the unsold donkeys.

It was not till he was almost at the gate of his own home that Kirk remembered the turquoise shop. There was no use thinking of it now, with the money all spent. Here it was, his mother's birthday, and he had no gift for her.

Wondering what to do next, Kirk took the key from his pocket and unlocked the street gate. There was the crunch of small feet on pebbled driveways as Johnny came running to meet his big brother. But Johnny's eyes rested on the small white donkey. He flung his arms around the neck of the little animal that was exactly right size for him.

"I'll call him Peter," announced Johnny, looking the donkey over. Peter's damp nose nuzzled Johnny as though to say he liked his new name.

"Back safely?" Mother called from the porch. She walked through the garden to join her boys near the gate.

"Oh, Mother, I'm so sorry," said Kirk. "I didn't mean to buy the donkey. I meant to buy you some turquoise jewelry for your birthday. But I saw the donkey. And a horrid man wanted to buy him. First thing I knew, I'd spent every rial I had saved for your birthday present.

"Oh, thank you, Kirk!" His mother's eyes were smiling, bluer than turquoise. "A baby donkey is exactly what I needed for my birthday!"

"Don't make fun of me, please!" wailed Kirk.

"Anyone could think of turquoise," said his mother. "Only a smart boy could think of a baby donkey. Look at Johnny and see what I mean.

Kirk looked. Johnny was talking into the twitching white ears while he hugged his new friend. He had lost the lonely expression that had been growing on him. He was happy again, just as he had been for the few weeks that the puppy had been small and gentle enough to play with him instead of knocking him down.

"Don't you remember the only thing a mother wants for her birthday?" Kirk's mother asked. The boy began to understand that queer thing she had said about mothers wanting nothing more than to know that their children were happy.

"Now let's get soap flakes and make a good warm suds," she said. "If Johnny and Peter are going to be such very close friends, we have to scrub away the germs."

So into the suds went Peter. And out he came, the whitest ball of fluff that ever ran around on four slim legs to follow a little master who was just the right size for him.

(The boy who bought the birthday donkey for his mother is now a college student. We shall keep his name a secret.)

Jasvant's Vacation

"I'll carry this!" Jasvant grasped his large flat package. The turbaned Sikh driver tossed the boy's bundle of clothes into the frame on the bus top.

"Is it too good to ride with the other baggage?" The tall Sikh stroked his black beard and stared at the package that was so treasured by its twelve-year-old owner.

Jasvant crowded into the old bus, already full of boys in loose white cotton trousers and shirts. They were leaving the Christian school for summer vacation in their homes in the Punjab of North India. Several boys, all older than Jasvant, proudly carried flat packages like his. They sat three in a seat, crowded the aisles, and climbed on the hood. The bus sputtered and rattled. The horn honked. Boys shouted. Vacation had begun.

The bus chugged across the plain between fields of corn, cotton, and melons. It met motor cars and trucks, brightly decorated covered carriages drawn by little horses, and wooden-wheeled carts drawn by humpbacked bullocks or sleepy bulffalo. There were men on horseback and men afoot, Hindus of all castes from Brahman to Sweeper. Women walked gracefully, balancing baskets or eathenware jars on modestly veiled heads.

The bus stopped for boys to get out at villages or at cart tracks leading to villages. Always the boys with the large flat packages carried them as something precious. Jasvant left the bus at the cart track to his home village. His bare feet followed a trail between fields of shoulder-high corn. Across the plain he saw the herdboys of his village, tending the cows and buffaloes of his neighbors. He wondered if they would be part of his vacation plan. Near his village he greeted the garden watchman on his high platform under its thatched roof. The boy turned to the settlement of Christian families on a fringe of the village.

"Jasvant is home!" ran from house to house. Women glanced up from grinding or spinning. Children left play. Neighbors poured from mud brick homes into the narrow, winding lane to greet him. Jasvant let an admiring child carry one bundle but held tightly to the flat package.

Alone with his parents, Jasvant opened it. Proudly he spread big charts with letters and pictures on them. The same groups of large letters were repeated over and over on the charts. The same syllables were repeated in different combinations beside the picture of the objects whose Hindi names they spelled. There were harder charts with more printing and fewer pictures. Jasvant had paper-covered books, too—primers, *Arrand the Wise Man,* and *Story of Jesus.*

His father, who went to school two years as a boy, nodded wisely. Jasvant's mother, who had never been to school, asked, "What are they?"

"Literacy charts. I'm the youngest boy of our school chosen to teach literacy this vacation," said Jasvant.

"Son, I am proud!" She looked bewildered. "What is literacy?"

"Knowing how to read," explained the boy. "We will teach many people this summer. Each learner promises to teach another."

"You will have school in our village?" His father seemed doubtful. "How? You are only a boy!"

"I can read. I have learned how to teach others."

"Who will come to your school?" wondered his mother. "Who will believe the barber's son is a teacher?"

The barber studied his son. "Perhaps some will come. Reading is good—but very hard."

The pastor stood at the door. "Reading is very good," he said. "Welcome home, Jasvant. I see your charts and books, Jasvant. I have heard of this new method. I forget what it is called."

"The Laubach method," Jasvant told him. "Frank Laubach, an American, has gone all over the world making charts of different languages and showing teachers how to use them."

"And each new reader teaches another," the pastor remembered. "That is Christian sharing. It is good. I will tell the people at evening prayers."

So, when the sun was setting that night and the two short pieces of old iron rails were pounded together to ring the Christians to prayer, the pastor told about Jasvant's vacation plan. The news started a buzz of excited talk.

"I would like to read," said an old man. "I've been poor all my life because I put my thumbprint on a paper at the money-lender's without knowing what was written."

"If I could read," said a mother, "I would not have to go to the scribe in the market place whenever a letter comes from my son in the army. I could write to him, too."

"Could we learn to read newspapers and books?" asked one.

"And stories from the Bible?" asked another.

The few literates told the others of the new doors reading would open. Then the iron rails banged again, and prayers began.

In the following days, Jasvant's father helped spread the news. He told of the literacy school to the Hindus beyond the settlement of Christians. Even the long-haired and bearded Sikhs, who never needed a barber, heard from others. There was something new to discuss as men or women met.

"I never went to school when I was a boy," a grown man said. "I had to help my father in the fields."

"I started school, but I grew tried of repeating the same words without understanding," another would say. "This new way of reading sounds better."

"In our village there was no school till the Christians came," said another. "Then I was too old for school."

"Do you suppose *we* could learn?" the women asked each other. "What would our husbands say?"

The excitement grew as the pastor told them there would be a celebration at the end of the summer. "On Literacy Sunday, we will honor all new readers." Hints were dropped about the plans for the ceremony—but only hints.

Jasvant chose a neem tree for the living roof of his summer schoolroom. The long narrow leaves of its low-spreading branches made good shade against the sun which shines its hottest in the Punjab. The "plup-plup" of the falling yellow neem berries made a comfortable sound. The boy set his charts and waited for his pupils. The first day he faced a crowd—grandmothers and babies, old men with dim eyes and tiny boys with wiggles, boys and girls his age or older. They wandered in to see what was happening and many wandered away again.

"The mission school was not like this!" a weary Jasvant told the pastor at the close of the first class. "I cannot teach a crowd that moves about and chatters!"

"It will be better soon," the pastor encouraged him. "Only those who mean to learn will keep coming."

The pastor was right. Soon Jasvant had two classes hard at work. Daytimes, women and children studied under the shade of the neem tree. Evenings, men and older boys worked by the soft light of string wicks burning in tins of mustard oil. Neither class was like the mission school. Women came late because their grinding and churning took so long, or because they had been working in the fields since sunrise. They left early to gather grass, twigs, and dried brush for firewood. While studying the charts, they nursed their babies or twirled their spindles to make cotton thread. In the evening, the men and older boys yawned after their long day of work under the hot Indian sun. Some dozed off to sleep. Others slipped away at the music of drums.

When Jasvant was discouraged, the pastor reminded him, "Reading will change life for the few who learn. Each learner will teach another." Soon Jasvant heard of these unseen readers.

A young bride shyly told him, "Each day as we weave or churn together, I tell my mother-in-law what you teach us."

An older woman told Jasvant proudly, "I am teaching my husband to read. He said he was too old to come to your school."

A herder boy told Jasvant at the evening class, "While we tend cattle, I teach the other boys what I learn in class. They want to come, too."

As summer went on, the better students progressed from charts to primers, then to the reader *Arrand the Wise Man,* and finally to the Hindi translation of *Story of Jesus.* Some read the first six of the little books with pictures of Jesus on each paper cover. They could read the next six by themselves. As Literacy

Sunday drew nearer, the pastor and Jasvant told them that the celebration would be a Festival of Lights, a Christian *Diwali*.

They all knew about the *Diwali* of the Hindus, the celebration of good winning over evil, of light winning over darkness. Though Christians would not burn saucer lamps and dance before an ugly clay image of the Hindu goddess Lakshmi, they loved the old custom of decorating their homes with rows and rows of saucer lamps, of painting designs of dyed clay on the walls, of marching through the streets in a gay lamp-carrying procession while bands played and everyone sang. The people of Jasvant's church wondered and waited for the Christian *Diwali* on Literacy Sunday.

"Be at your homes when the committee comes to give your reading test," was all that Jasvant would say. But a secret cannot be kept when many people need to know it. The singers had to know why they were practicing psalms set to Indian tunes. The bagpipe player had to know why he must gather players to form a band. The potter had to be told why the small saucer lamps ordered by the church must be of the best. Even the man who sold mustard oil for the lamps was taken into the secret which he promptly shared with his customers. Jasvant told his parents, and the barber often forgot it was a secret.

On Literacy Sunday, the courtyard of every hopeful reader was decorated with flowers and wall pictures. Every woman and girl had draped her prettiest *dapati* over her head. Every saucer lamp was filled with mustard oil and a good wick.

The iron rails in the churchyard were pounded, warning all new readers to be in their homes for their test. The music began— drums, bugles, bagpipes, and singers winding through the lanes. The lights of the singers flickered. In this Christian *Diwali* the songs praised the God of Love, not the clay goddess Lakshmi.

Jasvant marched and sang psalms set to Indian folk tunes. He praised God for the chance to open the doors of reading to his neighbors. He was more nervous than his pupils over their tests.

Each of them worried only once. He worried for each pupil, and for the pupils of his pupils.

The music grew louder and the procession lights grew brighter as many villagers joined in the marching. At each stop musicians and others crowded into the courtyard. The pastor took one of the booklets of *Story of Jesus* and chose a chapter for the test. Jasvant would scarcely breathe while his pupil read. Each one who passed was given an unlighted saucer lamp. The pastor would lower his own burning *diwa* to the new reader's. The light would pass from one lamp to the other. Jasvant wondered how many times the light that came from reading would pass from his pupils to others.

"March ahead of the band," each new reader was told.

One by one the new readers' lamps were lighted. A few failed, but only a few. Jasvant suffered with each one as he faced the test. He rejoiced with each one as the lamps were lighted. He praised God with each one as they wound through the lanes of the village, celebrating the Christian Festival of Lights, singing

> The Lord God is King.
> He is the King of Glory.

(This story was suggested by Lilly Swords, missionary in Hissar, Punjab. She gave all the background material.)

Chung

It was not Chung's fault that he was being shut up in a damp, brick, prisonlike beggar's home. His only fault was not being good at begging. He was not worth his keep to the hard-faced Chinese woman who had been taking care of him in her poor, dark home in beautiful green Taiwan.

Even after the accident that left Chung's legs mere stumps a few inches below his knees, he was a failure as a beggar. Some boys are not born to hold out hands and whine for pennies, and Chung was one of these.

Chung's luck was not all bad. He had the good luck to be brought to the jaillike beggars' home at just the time when a Canadian missionary, Mrs. Dickson, was there to see what she could do to help the prisoners and the beggars.

"Not here!" she said when she saw the woman giving Chung to the keeper of the beggars' home. The boy felt loved for the first time he could remember as she looked at him. "That child must not be left here."

Chung knew that the woman who had brought him was already scurrying away. He felt no homesickness as he watched her disappear around a corner in her high-necked blouse and loose cotton pants.

Chung heard the caretaker of the beggars' home answer Mrs. Dickson, "Where else can the child go? That woman will not feed him any longer. He is lucky to have this beggars' home for a roof and our rice for his food. Living here is better than sitting in a doorway holding out an empty rice bowl. Who else would shelter a child with only stubs for legs?"

Chung shivered as he looked at the place that would be his home. It was even worse than the rickety hovel where he had lived with the sullen-faced woman who always scolded and complained about the rice he ate. Then Chung looked up at his new friend, the kind-faced woman who was saying, "I will find a place for this child to live."

There was something in her voice that made Chung know she would find a home for him. And he was right.

Before the sun went down that evening, Chung was eating rice, cabbage, and duck eggs in his new home with thirty-five other boys. When he was sitting in a chair at the friendly, big table, he could almost forget that his legs stopped just a few inches below his knees. When Chung needed to go anywhere, there was always a big boy ready to carry him on his back like a baby. It was days before Chung could teach the other boys that he could really totter about on his stubs of legs. It hurt, of course, because the amputations had not been made by a good surgeon. But Chung could manage.

Quickly Chung learned to trust his new friends—the thirty-five boys who treated him like a brother, the young Chinese orphanage director who was like a father to them all, and Sister Alma the German nurse in her blue and white uniform who was like a mother to the orphan boys and to the patients in the leprosy hospital across the highway.

Being loved was new to Chung. It felt good to know that someone cared that he had only short stumps for legs.

"I will make wooden legs for Chung," offered one of the patients in the leprosarium across the highway.

"But first he must have an operation. The stumps must be smooth to fit the new wooden legs without hurting him too much," said the doctor who visited the orphanage.

After the operation, the patient in the leprosarium did his best, but he did not have enough skill. It takes more than a good and willing carpenter to make new legs on which a boy can walk and run. The new wooden legs hurt Chung. He could still walk better in a pair of rubber-soled, canvas shoes on his stubs of legs. He wore the toes of the shoes pointing backward to help him balance.

The years went by and Chung still walked on the stubs in rubber-soled shoes. He managed somehow to pull himself onto the bus that carried the orphanage boys to school. He could swing a long knife or a short-handled hoe in the garden that covered the hillside in back of the orphanage. He could join in the games. He could do his share to clean the rice or chop the cabbage or cut the fish for the orphanage meals. He was proud to know that he was one of the best students in his class at school.

One fear, however, came to Chung more often as he grew older—twelve years—thirteen years—fourteen years. "What will happen when I am too old to live here? What job is there for a man with only stubs for legs?"

So, it was a big day for Chung when Walter Tong brought supplies to the orphanage. Boxes of American food came often—dried milk, corn meal, flour, meals-for-millions, cheese. Usually Mr. Tong was too busy to come with these boxes labelled Church World Service.

Luckily he arrived in time to see Chung roll off the bus and waddle up the hilly walk toward the orphanage, hobbling along on his stumps in their rubber-soled, canvas shoes worn backward. Chung could not understand what Mr. Tong was saying in English to the German nurse and the Chinese orphanage director. He could understand very well, however, when his teacher turned to him and spoke in Chinese.

"Chung," he said, "the American will take you in his car to a place where Chinese refugees from the Mainland are making the very best artificial legs. He will find out if they can make a pair for you. You will go next Sunday afternoon."

It was an excited Chung who rode in the American's blue jeep station wagon to the Nanking Rehabilitation Center in Taiwan's capital city, Taipei. He was almost too excited to notice the sun sparkling in the wet rice fields, the children playing in the yards of low U-shaped brick homes, the patient water buffaloes and oxen dragging their wagons loaded with charcoal or bamboo poles, or the ducks splashing in the irrigation ditches. Reaching Taipei, his eyes popped wide as their car maneuvered among bicycles, buses, military jeeps, and pedicabs pulled by men pedaling hard on big tricycles.

It was a happy Chung who was welcomed by a kindly Christian, George Yu-Chieh Tson, Director of the Nanking Rehabilitation Center. Chung watched wide-eyed, as men, minus one or both legs, learned to walk on artificial legs.

"You are lucky," these men told Chung. "You still have your knees to bend. You have a little leg below your knee for fastening on your new legs. Some of us had amputations above our knees. You are lucky."

"We will come back some weekday to have Chung's measurements taken," said Mr. Tong.

"We will take them now," said Mr. Tson. Then even though it was late on Sunday afternoon, Mr. Tson and his helpers measured Chung so that they could make artificial legs that would be comfortable to wear.

Riding home, daydreaming of his new legs, Chung was worried about one thing. "I do not have any money to pay," he said. "Don't new legs cost many dollars?"

"Many dollars," agreed Mr. Tong, "but you need not think of that. A man who loves children has sent money for special things—like legs for a boy who is a good student and is growing to be a fine young man."

So now Chung can stand tall with the other boys who are almost man-size. He can walk erect with his head as high as theirs. He knows that when the time comes to leave the orphange, he can face the world as a whole man—unashamed.

(In 1956 I met Chung in the World Vision Orphanage near Taipei, and learned his story from Walter Tong who was then directing Church World Service activities in Taiwan.)

Lola's Song

Nenet balanced the flat basket of yellow fruit steadily on her head. She started down the steep bamboo ladder from her grandmother's house that stood on six strong posts in a little Philippine village by a wide, brown river.

"Thank you, Lola," she called to her grandmother from the

lowest step. "We all like the *santol* fruit, and yours is the best *santol* tree in our village. This basket will be empty before dark. Thank you."

"Do not thank me, Nenet," said Lola. "Thank the good God who makes fruit grow. Thank God who cares for you and for all his creatures."

Then Nenet's grandmother began singing one of her favorite songs. The words followed the girl as her wooden sandals went clip-clip-clip down the shady village road:

> How strong and sweet my Father's care
> That round about me like the air,
> Is with me always, everywhere.
> He cares for me.

"Why does Lola always talk as if God was right here in our own village taking care of us?" wondered Nenet.

Just then there was quacking beside her. From the yard of her grandmother's neighbor waddled ten black and white ducks. In a long line they crossed the road in front of her. They quacked and waddled through the yard of Ramon straight to the banks of the wide, brown river. Down the path they fluttered into the river for a swim and a meal. They dove for food. They wiggled their tails while their heads were under water. They looked so happy in the brown river that Nenet found herself singing Lola's song for them—with a new ending:

> How strong and sweet my Father's care
> That round about me like the air,
> Is with me always, everywhere.
> He cares for *ducks*.

Nenet stood on the edge of the stream watching the ducks. Across the wide, brown river she saw a hot and weary carabao being led by Farmer Juan for a bath. This big water buffalo had been dragging the plow in the muddy rice fields since the first light of morning. He was tired and thirsty. Nenet could imagine a contented look on the carabao's broad face as Juan splashed the welcome water over the hot animal's wide, gray back. The carabao sank down, down into the river till nothing but the breathing tip of his wide nose showed. Nenet found herself singing Lola's song for the carabao—with a new ending:

> How strong and sweet my Father's care
> That round about me like the air,
> Is with me always, everywhere.
> He cares for *carabaos*.

Then Nenet remembered the basket of *Santol* fruit she was carrying home. She hurried back onto the road shaded by its rows of trees. A gray and white butterfly flew over her head. It fluttered toward a *calacuchi* tree with its shiny dark leaves and its golden-hearted white blossoms. It rested on a fragrant flower and began to suck the sweet nectar. The butterfly's striped wings were at rest as the little thing tasted the good food meant especially for soaring butterflies and twittering sun birds. Nenet found herself singing Lola's song for the butterfly—with a new ending:

> How strong and sweet my Father's care
> That round about me like the air,
> Is with me always, everywhere.
> He cares for *butterflies*.

Walking on, Nenet almost stumbled over a red and brown hen scratching for food for her ten newly hatched chicks. They were so tiny, so helpless, so fresh from their shells! Nenet wanted to put them in her basket and carry them home to take care of them. Then she watched the mother hen and knew that the chicks were safe. It was God's plan that hens should know how to care for their babies till they were able to scratch for their own food. Nenet found herself singing Lola's song with another new ending:

> How strong and sweet my Father's care
> That round about me like the air,

> Is with me always, everywhere.
> He cares for *chicks*.

Nenet took the last bend in the road before her own thatched house that stood high above the ground on its six posts. She saw her brother Pedring carrying Baby Rosita away from the dangers of a deep mud hole. She saw her father cutting bamboo logs to build a new room for their house, and singing as he swung his sharp bolo knife. She saw the tree full of ripe avocados that were so good to eat. She saw the ducks that laid enough eggs for her family and some more to sell in market. She saw, tethered under the house, the little black pig that would taste so good at fiesta time. She heard the clack-clack of her mother's wooden loom, weaving firm, white cloth. She saw the smoke rolling from the fireplace of the kitchen lean-to, and smelled the rice and fish cooking. Nenet's world was good—very, very good.

Then Nenet found herself singing her grandmother's song— just as Lola sang it:

> How strong and sweet my Father's care
> That round about me like the air,
> Is with me always, everywhere.
> He cares for *me*.

(This story was written in "a little Philippine village by a wide, brown river" while I watched the same ducks, carabao, butterflies, and chickens that Nenet saw.)

III

Yesterday's Boys and Girls

A New Name

Titus and Simeon were friends. They played together in the cypress gardens of Antioch, capital city of Syria and third largest city in the great Roman Empire. They wandered together through the market place where Syrian, Jewish, and Greek merchants sat in their booths. They walked together through the wheat fields and vineyards that grew in the fertile valley of the Orontes River. There were no better friends in all Antioch than the Greek boy Titus and the Jewish boy Simeon.

There were many times, however, when the two boys could not be together. Simeon went to the synagogue school to learn Jewish laws, Jewish history, and Jewish prophecies from the rabbis. Titus studied about the greatness of Greece in a school with a Greek teacher. On the Jewish Sabbath, Simeon always went to the synagogue school to hear the rabbi read from the books of the law and the prophets. Titus had no regular time to worship, but he sometimes went with his parents to the shrine of the Greek sun god, Apollo.

Titus and Simeon were sorry that they could not study and worship together, but there was nothing they could do about it. Titus was a Greek. Simeon was a Jew. And that was that.

One day Simeon ran to his friend's house of sun-dried mud bricks. He had exciting news. "There were strangers in the synagogue yesterday."

"There are always strangers in Antioch," answered Titus.

"We see strangers whenever we go to the shrine of Apollo."

"But these strangers were different," Simeon insisted. "They were going to be killed or thrown into prison in Jerusalem. So they ran away."

"Then they are bad men?" Titus began to see Simeon had a real story.

"No! They are good men—*very* good men!"

"Then why are they running away?"

"They believe a new religion. The Jewish leaders in Jerusalem do not like it. They do not like to see Jews following new leaders. My father says they are jealous of the new ones."

"But I don't understand," said Titus. "You say the strangers were driven away from Jerusalem because of their religion. Aren't they afraid they will be driven away from Antioch? There are Jewish leaders here too. Why do the strangers talk about their religion here? It would be safer for them to keep still. I don't understand."

"You would understand if you saw them," said Simeon. "They are excited about their new belief. They love their new leader— a man called Jesus Christ who died but is alive again. They just have to tell other folks about him."

"What will the Jews of Antioch do?" asked Titus. "Are you going to let them go into your synagogue to talk about this new religion?"

"We are letting them talk," said Simeon. "Some Jews like what they say. Others hate anything that is new. My father likes them. He thinks the strangers are wise and good."

"I wish I could see them," said Titus. "But a Greek could not go to a Jewish synagogue."

"Of course not," agreed Simeon. "Now let's go to the river to see what boats are there."

Another day it was Titus' turn to run to Simeon's house with an exciting story. "There were strangers in the house of our Greek neighbor yesterday," he began.

Simeon started to say, "There are always strangers in Antioch," but he saw the happy face of Titus. "Tell me about them," he said.

"They were driven from Jerusalem, just like the strangers in your synagogue. They, too, are Jews that followed Jesus Christ who was crucified and lives again. But they are Jews who were born on the big Greek island of Cyprus. They speak Greek. They are telling the Greeks and Greek-speaking Jews of Antioch about their new religion."

Titus and Simeon were smiling their widest smiles at each other.

"Are the Greeks listening to them?" asked Simeon.

"We are crowding about them to listen," answered Titus.

"Do the Greeks believe that the God of Jesus Christ is greater than Apollo, the sun god?"

"Many believe," answered Titus. "My father says he wants to hear more. He lets me go with him."

After that the two boys could be together more. Titus dared go with Simeon to the synagogue to hear the strangers from Jerusalem talk in the Jewish language about Jesus Christ. Simeon dared go to the Greek halls or homes or market booths where the other strangers from Jerusalem spoke in Greek about the new religion of hope and love. More and more people, both Jews and Greeks, heard and believed.

One day a new teacher named Barnabas came. The church in Jerusalem had sent him to help the new church at Antioch. Everyone liked Barnabas. He was the sort of man who had a talent for seeing the best in people. While he was preaching in Antioch, Barnabas remembered Paul, the man who knew so well how to preach to Greeks. So Barnabas went to Tarsus to find Paul and bring him to Antioch.

For a whole year Paul and Barnabas met with the church at Antioch. And Titus and Simeon were as good members of the church as any of the men and women.

71

One day Titus said to Simeon, "We go to the same church now, but we still have different names. You are still a Jew and I am still a Greek or Gentile."

Then Simeon laughed. "That is not true any longer. We have the same name now. My father heard it in the market place. The Jews who do not believe in Jesus Christ have given us a new nickname. They use it when they laugh at us."

"A nickname?" asked Titus. "What is it?"

"Christians! They call us Christians."

"Christians—Christians." Titus repeated the name slowly.

"It means the people that belong to Jesus Christ."

"It is a good name."

The boys smiled at each other. It was the smile of good friends who were becoming even better friends. They tried calling each other by the new name—their name.

"Christian!"

"Christian!"

(Source: Acts 11:19-26.)

New Sharing

Simeon, Jewish boy of Antioch, and Titus, Greek boy of Antioch, were better friends than ever. Now they had the same name, *Christian*. They had always played together, but now they went to church together also. Sometimes Titus went to the synagogue school with Simeon. Learning about the Jewish laws, history, and prophecies helped him understand what the men from Jerusalem told about the religion of Jesus Christ. He learned how the faith of the Christians had grown out of the Jewish faith. Now, he learned, it was reaching out to people of other faiths, even people like himself who had been taught to worship the sun god, Apollo.

Titus liked the stories of the Jewish prophets that he heard in the synagogue school. The prophets were men who lived so close to God that they had messages from God to the people. Titus liked best the prophet that told that some day a Savior would come: "His name shall be called Wonderful, Counsellor, . . . The Prince of Peace." These were beautiful words, but not so beautiful as the words Jesus Christ had said when he came to earth: "For God so loved the world that he gave his only begotten Son, that whosoever believeth in him should not perish, but have everlasting life." Titus and Simeon thought that the news brought by the Christians was greater than anything they learned at synagogue school.

Having learned about the prophets of old, the boys were not surprised at news that spread through Antioch. Men called prophets had come from Jerusalem. They were telling what was going to happen. One of these prophets was named Agabus. He had bad news.

"There will be a great famine soon," he said. "Crops will fail. There will not be enough to eat."

If such news had come to Antioch before there was a Christian church there, the people would all have busied themselves laying up food for their own families. Each man would have been thinking about himself and his own household. But the Christians of Antioch did not think of themselves first. They thought first of the Christians in Jerusalem who had already suffered for their faith in Jesus Christ.

"Think of the boys and girls in Jerusalem whose fathers have been killed or dragged off to prison," said Titus' father. "They are poor now. They cannot store food for famine days."

"There is too much suffering already among the Christians in Jerusalem," Simeon's father agreed. "Perhaps Agabus is right about the famine. Perhaps he is wrong. Whether he is right or wrong, we should help the Christians in Jerusalem."

The church at Antioch agreed.

"I am not rich, but I will give what I can," said the father of Titus.

"I have a large family to feed, but I can spare something for the Christians at Jerusalem," said the father of Simeon.

Fathers, mothers, and children agreed. Boys and girls thought of ways to earn or save money.

"Barnabas and Paul will be the ones to take the gift," suggested someone. All agreed. The Christians of Antioch did more than send relief money. They sent it by the two men who were helping most in their church. They shared their best with the church in Jerusalem.

The church at Antioch did not sit still waiting till its two greatest leaders, Paul and Barnabas, came back from the long trip to Jerusalem. When a church has learned to share, it grows. The Christian men talked about their church in the market place and brought men to join them. The Christian women met other women at the fountain where they filled their water jars, told them about the new faith, and brought them to the new church.

Christian children said to their playmates, "Come to our church with us. You will like it." So, men, women, and children were added to the church.

Finally Barnabas and Paul came back from Jerusalem. The people of the Antioch church gathered together to hear news of the church in Jerusalem. They were glad to meet a new worker, John Mark, the young nephew of Barnabas.

One day when the Christians were gathered together there was a special feeling that God was with them. The men and women felt it. The boys and girls felt it too. Titus and Simeon sat side by side, and they felt God's nearness. As the church worshiped and prayed, God's Holy Spirit came into the Christians' minds and hearts with a new idea.

They seemed to hear God's voice saying, "Set Barnabas and Paul apart for me for a task to which I have called them."

The Christians had shared their money. They had shared their leaders, Paul and Barnabas, for the trip to Jerusalem. Now God was calling them to share their glad news with others who had not heard it. He had chosen Barnabas and Paul to spread the religion of Jesus Christ.

Again the people prayed and fasted. They promised God that the church of Antioch would send Barnabas and Paul to carry the good news. The Christians helped Barnabas and Paul prepare for their adventuresome journey. Then they gathered to watch them start. Simeon and Titus stood side by side watching their friends till they were out of sight.

"Simeon," Titus said in his remembering voice. "Once I asked you why the strangers from Jerusalem did not stop talking about Jesus Christ so they would be safe in Antioch. Now I understand."

And Simeon agreed. "Loving Jesus Christ makes anyone want to share."

(Source: Acts 11:27-30; 13:1-3.)

The Church Everybody Built

Rolf and Hans sat side by side in their little cart to rest. They had dragged away their last load of chips from the hammers of the stonemasons. The boys gazed with awe at the tall and beautiful church they had helped build. They were German boys of the years called the Middle Ages, the years when people showed their love of the Church by building great cathedrals or smaller churches that were full of beauty. Some of these churches, six hundred or more years old, still stand in Europe and Britain today.

The master wood carver smiled at the boys. "You can be proud!" he said. "You have worked as hard as any of us. It is a beautiful church we have built!"

"Oh, we only dragged stone and wood and tools." Rolf did not like to show how happy he was at praise from Heinrich, the master wood carver. "The church is beautiful because of the stonemasons and wood carvers . . ."

Hans finished Rolf's sentence, "And the stone carvers and the men who make stained-glass windows."

"But what could we have done if the men and women had not hauled the big stones and timbers in their big carts—if you boys and girls had not dragged the small stones in your small carts?" The master wood carver looked at the spire pointing so straight skyward. "That is what makes a church—everybody working together. It makes a beautiful church—a happy church —a growing church."

Heinrich sat on the grass beside the boys. He could relax after the long weeks and months of carving to make the doors and the inner walls of the church beautiful. It seemed to the boys a good time to ask questions. There were many things they wanted to know.

"I know why we built this church," Rolf began. "There were too many of us for the little old building. Besides the Baron wanted a big church. He offered to give us land and materials if we would do the work."

"That is right," agreed the master wood carver.

"But I have often wondered how the Church came here in the first place," said Rolf.

"Come inside the church for that story." The master wood carver led the way. The boys walked on tiptoe in the quietness under the arched roof. They loved the colored sunlight streaming through the stained-glass windows telling Bible stories about Abraham, Joseph, David, Amos, and Jesus. Few of the people of that town could read, and the Bible was opened only by the priests. It was good to have the stories in the beautiful windows.

Hans and Rolf followed Heinrich between the pillars decorated by the apprentice wood carvers. They stood in front of a pair of wall panels carved by the master wood carver himself.

One panel showed a man chopping down a giant oak tree. The other showed the same man, with helpers, building a small church.

"We have wondered about these carvings," said Hans. "We wanted to ask you while you were at work, but our mothers told us to stay away."

"Who is the man chopping down the tree in one picture and building the little church in the other picture?" asked Rolf.

"His name was Winfrid then. Later the Pope named him Saint Boniface. He was in a monastery in England about a hundred years after Augustine went there from Rome. He was a brave man. He liked to adventure for the Church. He was not satisfied with the quiet and easy life of the monastery. He wanted something harder to do for God and the Church.

"So he crossed the sea to Germany and went among the pagan tribes. He found they worshiped a god called Woden. They believed this Woden was very powerful and very much to be feared. They were afraid of sacred places that they thought belonged to him.

"Winfrid learned that one of these sacred places was a huge oak tree." Heinrich pointed to the oak in the wood carving. "The German pagans worshiped that tree. If anything should happen to it, they thought great trouble would come to them all. They believed anyone who hurt that tree would be struck down instantly.

"One day the people gathered under the oak tree of Woden to worship their god. Winfrid was with them. He had tried to tell

77

them of his religion of love, but nobody would listen. They were afraid of Woden. They would not hear of any other faith.

"Winfrid saw his chance to prove that Woden had no power. Bravely he walked up to the great oak tree. He raised his axe. He struck a mighty blow.

"The people were horrified. They screamed. They scattered in the forest.They expected to see the earth crack apart—or fire fall from the skies—or some terrible disaster. At least, they thought, Winfrid would be struck dead.

"The people covered their eyes and their ears. They trembled. They prayed to Woden to spare them.

"But nothing happened—nothing but the steady clop-clop of Winfrid's axe on the trunk of the great oak tree. The pagans were hiding in the forest when the tree crashed to the ground. But it was not a magical crash. It was the same sound that any old oak tree would make as it fell. Rotten at its heart, the tree splintered into many pieces.

"Slowly the people crept back from their hiding places in the forest. They stood about Winfrid gazing at the man who was not afraid of Woden. For the first time, they listened as he told them about the God of love whom he worshiped."

Heinrich led the boys to the second carved panel. It was the picture of the same Winfrid, with many helpers, building a small church in the spot where the great oak had fallen.

"This picture tells the rest of the story," said Heinrich.

"I can guess," said Hans. "Winfrid used the wood from the great oak tree to build a church where the new Christians could worship the God of Jesus Christ."

"They must have been glad," said Rolf slowly, "to know a God that loved them instead of a god that scared them."

Hans and Rolf gazed with awe at the church that rose with such dignity and beauty over their heads. They had been proud of the church while they and their small cart helped build it. They were even more proud of it now. They thought how brave men had brought Christianity to Germany. They were glad that they belonged to a growing church—a brave church—a beautiful church.

(Suggested by reference in Walter Russell Bowie's *The Story of the Church* to boys using their carts to help build some of the big churches of the Middle Ages.)

Jacob Earns His Salt

The berries poured in a rich blue stream from Peter's pail, from Patience's pail, even from little Jonathan's pail. Jacob watched them go rolling into the big tin pan. Then he looked at his own bucket. He saw the bottom of the pail showing between the berries. Oh, if Mother would only look the other way while he poured his berries into her pan!

"What pies we can make!" Mother stood in the door of the cabin of logs smiling at the children as the berries mounted in the pan. She turned toward Jacob. "And what have you for the pies, my oldest son?"

Hesitating, Jacob came forward with his light pail. "There was a pair of robins feeding their babies in a nest in a thorn-apple tree," said Jacob. "I was watching them and forgot to pick many berries."

He emptied his pail slowly, hoping that two or three at a time the berries might look like more. Dribble, dribble they slid into the pan. There were so few of them that they made almost no difference in the pile.

"Jacob," sighed his mother. "When will you learn that in a pioneer land like ours everyone must do his work! It isn't as though we had stores or near neighbors. As a picker of blueberries, my son, you surely are not worth your salt."

Patience saw Jacob's blush of shame. Adoring her big brother,

79

she understood why he so often forgot to do his part. She loved him for all the exciting things he saw in the woods and the fields, but of course what Mother said was true. Perhaps she could help him by changing the subject quickly.

"Oh, Mother!" Patience exclaimed. "What you said about salt reminds me. Have the Indians brought any salt yet?"

"No!" Mother's face under her white muslin cap was worried. "It was ten days ago that I told them we would soon need salt, and they have not brought any yet. They are busy with their own crops and berries. They do not care if we have to eat potatoes and fish without salt.

"If we only knew where they get it," mused Peter for the hundredth time, "we should not have to wait for them. It can't be far away. They are sometimes back with salt only a few hours after you ask for it."

"Yes, it must be within a few miles," agreed Mother. "The men have searched all around for it and cannot find a trace. There is not even a salt lick for cattle. When they ask the Indians where it is, they just grunt and say they will bring some."

"It is lucky the Indians are our friends," said Peter.

Jacob had been only half listening. He had heard this wondering about salt many times before. He was busy making plans of his own.

"Mother," he said, "I am going back to the berry patch. I'll fill my pail till it pours out on all sides!"

"Be home for dinner. You can watch the sun." Mother looked proudly after the sturdy boy as he started resolutely up the path. She had hated to scold him. Like Patience, she loved him for his joy in all that grew in woods or fields. But he must learn that a pioneer's life is full of work.

"Not worth my salt—not worth my salt—" chanted itself accusingly over and over in Jacob's mind. He pushed his way through branches and underbrush on his way to the berry patch. He had heard that phrase used about some worthless settler. Now his own mother had used it about him. "Not worth my salt!"

"Even Baby Jonathan is a bigger help than I am. But I will show them. I will fill my pail to overflowing—today and every day. I *will* be worth my salt!"

Reaching the fields where the berries hung thick on their low bushes, Jacob set to work determined to turn aside for nothing. A cuckoo sang from a maple tree, but Jacob whistled so that he would not be tempted to listen. A squirrel ran chattering by. Jacob's eyes followed its gay journeyings, but he jerked them back to the berries and the pail. A snake went gliding through the grass. Jacob wondered where its home might be, but he would not let himself follow.

On and on he picked. The bottom of the pail was covered. The berries began to heap up in the pail. It looked like little Jonathan's pail. Steadily the berries went in. It looked like Patience's pail, then like Peter's pail. Drop-drop went the berries into the bucket, not one wandering into Jacob's mouth.

The pail was half full when Jacob heard a soft and rapid padding of feet coming along the narrow trail that followed the edge of the lake. He had often wondered where that Indian trail led, but had never strayed far enough from his own cabin to find out. He sat quiet as a stone among the bushes as the footfalls came nearer. Soon a tall Indian came in sight, walking quickly and silently along the trail. Jacob watched him pass and noticed the big wooden bucket he carried. Jacob wondered if the Indian knew a better blueberry patch. It was worth trying to find out. Berries were growing scarce near the cabin.

A boy who could follow thrushes or foxes through the woods could be quick and silent in more serious trailing. Peter could never have done it, nor Patience, with their careful, steady ways. Without another thought for his half-filled berry pail, Jacob began winding his way through the bushes. At first he did not dare to use the trail for fear he would be discovered. The Indians were friendly when the white men left them alone, but they might not like a white boy spying on one of their secrets.

After a few minutes, Jacob could not hear the Indian's footsteps. That meant he had been going faster than Jacob and was already out of hearing. The boy left the bushes and ran noiselessly along the trail.

He could not see the Indian but he could see signs of recent passing—a twig bent here, a toadstool crushed there. He felt sure he was following the man at a safe distance. Jacob hurried along the trail, fearing he would be discovered. He jumped as a partridge whirred into the air from a thicket close to his feet. There might be more Indians at the end of the trail.

Suddenly Jacob froze in his path, then slipped silently into the trees. Just in front of him the Indian was resting in a grassy spot not far from the trail. By the time Jacob was safely behind the broad trunk of an oak, the Indian was again on his feet. The man walked a few steps farther from the path, the bucket still in his hand. Then he went down on his knees and climbed into a deep hole.

Jacob could hear the click of a stone hatchet on yielding rock of some kind. He could see the tall feathers on the Indian's hair bobbing as he pounded. What could he be doing in such a hole?

Finally the Indian straightened and pulled himself out of the hole. He reached in and brought out the bucket heaped with something hard and white.

Jacob clapped his hands over his mouth to hold back a squeal. Many times he had seen such a bucket full of hard, white lumps brought to the cabin door by an Indian. He had heard his mother thank the Indian in her friendliest voice and give him something he valued in payment. It was precious rock salt in the bucket.

The Indian was back on the trail, retracing his steps. Jacob stayed behind his oak tree until the sounds of footsteps had passed beyond hearing. He waited a minute, and another, to be sure the Indian was well out of the way. Then he crept from behind the tree and toward the hole. Deep down he peered. In the hole, where the layers of dirt and rock had been cut away, was a rich supply of rock salt.

"If only I had an empty pail," thought Jacob. Then he looked at his berry pail and laughed. There were only three lonely berries left.

"I could follow my way home by the trail of berries," he chuckled as he jumped into the salt mine.

Jacob found it slow work to chip off the hard rocks of salt. There were soon enough small chunks in his pail to prove what he had found.

"Not worth my salt? Not worth my salt?" went chanting itself merrily through his head as he skipped proudly home. This time the chant made Jacob laugh. He knew he had proved himself worth his salt.

There was an excited crowd in Jacob's cabin that night as the settlers gathered to hear his story. Some urged that everyone should hurry to the salt mine with pick and pail to bring home a big supply. But the wiser heads won the argument against that plan. The crowd listened to Jacob's father.

"Let's go on just as we have done," urged Jacob's father. "The Indians cherish their secret. They do not need to know that we share it. We shall still ask them for salt and give them the trinkets they like in payment. If the time should ever come that the Indians will not bring us salt, we know where to find it."

A proud Jacob stood beside his father as the settlers filed out on their way to their own log cabins. There was thanks or praise from each. But the best praise of all came with his mother's good-night kiss.

"Well Jacob, my son," she said, "there are more ways than one to be worth our salt!"

(Note: Jacob is fictional but the salt deposits on the east shore of Cayuga Lake are real. Known only to the Indians in the days of the early settlers, they are still mined today.)

When Ben Franklin Stooped

The name, Benjamin Franklin, stands for many good things—love of country, common sense, honesty, generosity, thrift, wisdom. While he was growing up, however, Ben Franklin made plenty of mistakes. Like many clever boys, he thought he knew all the answers without any advice from anybody. He often quarreled with people whose ideas were not the same as his.

Working on his brother's newspaper gave him a chance to print what he thought. Though he was only seventeen years old, he seemed to feel that he knew more than others who had been studying and thinking for many years. He liked to make fun of important and well-known persons. These might be good men who were doing their best to make Boston a better city, but young Ben Franklin wrote unkindly about them.

Cotton Mather was one of the men whom the young writer and printer loved to ridicule. Cotton Mather was a famous Boston preacher. Ben Franklin, who had not yet begun to think much about religion, made a practice of disagreeing with this good man who was so much older and wiser than he.

At about this time, Ben Franklin went to Philadelphia to find work in a print shop. After a few months he came home to Boston for a visit. He was eighteen years old then. He had done so well in Philadelphia that he had a fine new suit of clothes, a big gold watch that he loved to draw from his pocket when people were watching, silver coins to jingle, a letter from the governor, and a good future in the printing business in Philadelphia. He did not mind letting others know how well he had been doing. He even strutted a bit.

For some reason, Ben Franklin decided to call in the home of the famous preacher Cotton Mather. Perhaps it was to visit the son, Samuel, who was just Ben's age. Perhaps it was to let the great man see what a success the young printer had become.

As the two men talked, the older one could not help knowing that the younger one was still proud and still sure that anyone who disagreed with him was wrong.

When the visit was over, Cotton Mather told his young guest that he could leave the house by a door at the end of a narrow passage. Now it happened that there was a crossbeam overhead in the passage. Ben Franklin was going first, turning his head to talk to Cotton Mather who followed him.

"Stoop! Stoop!" called Mr. Mather.

He did not explain why Ben Franklin should stoop. The young man was never quick to take orders from anyone. He did not stoop. Bang went his head against the crossbeam.

As Ben Franklin rubbed his bruised head, Cotton Mather saw his chance to tell the proud young man a truth he needed to know.

"You are young and have the world before you," said the older man. "*Stoop,* as you go through it, and you will miss many, hard thumps." Of course that was another way of saying, "Stop being so proud of yourself. Try being humble for a change."

Like many clever young men, Benjamin Franklin could learn a lesson, and remember it. He began to practice humility. In *Poor Richard's Almanac,* which he wrote every year for twenty-five years, there were many proverbs advising people to be humble and to see their own mistakes instead of the mistakes of others. Here are just a few of those sayings:

Wink at small faults—remember thou hast great ones.

He that falls in love with himself will have no rivals.

None but the well-bred man knows how to confess a fault.

Fools need advice most, but wise men only are the better for it.

The Proud hate Pride—in others.

E'er you remark another's sin, bid your conscience look within.

Sixty years after his lesson in stooping, Benjamin Franklin wrote a letter to Samuel, son of Cotton Mather. He told the story of the bumped head and the advice about stooping. Then Benjamin Franklin wrote, "This advice, thus beat into my head, has frequently been of use to me, and often I think of it when I see pride mortified and misfortunes brought upon people by carrying their heads too high."

(Source: *Autobiography of Benjamin Franklin*.)

The Pima Girl

This is a true story of an Indian girl of long ago. She belonged to the Pima tribe of Arizona. Her tribespeople were intelligent and friendly. They lived at peace with the white settlers and with most of their Indian neighbors. The tribe called Apaches, however, were their enemies. In those days the Apaches were a warlike tribe. They had terrifying habits of swooping upon a Pima village to plunder or to kill.

On one of these quick raids the Apaches killed the father of the Indian girl of our story. Naturally, she was terribly angry at the Apaches.

Usually the Pima women and girls stayed near their adobe cabins while the men went outside the village for any work that took courage. The women knew it was their own job to take care of their homes and their families. It was for the men, they knew, to do anything beyond their own Pima settlement.

The Pima girl was too angry to care about the custom of her tribe. She was so angry that she felt she must do something with her own hands.

The girl called the Pima men to her. "I must pay back the Apaches for killing my father," she told them. "In four days I will ride into their country. I will kill the first Apache that I see. Will you men ride with me?"

86

The men of the Pima tribe were not in the habit of taking orders from a sixteen-year-old girl. She was so very angry and so very brave, however, that they found themselves agreeing to follow her.

When the fourth day came, the Indian girl jumped on her buckskin-colored pony and galloped off, leading the men across the Arizona plain. Like them, she carried Indian weapons—a war club, a bow, arrows.

The Pimas thundered into Apache country. They sighted a lone Apache crossing the sage-brush desert. They did not know whether this particular Indian had ever raided a Pima village, but the Pima girl was too angry to care. He was an Apache and her enemy.

The Pima braves could have fought with the Apache, but the Pima girl had said that she must do it herself. Two of her tribesmen held the enemy Indian. The girl urged her buckskin-colored pony to its greatest speed. Raising her war club, she rode upon the Apache—and killed him.

On the slower ride back to the Pima village, the girl's anger changed to sick horror at what she had done. Back in her village, she did everything she could to wipe out the memory. She went through the Pima ceremonies that were supposed to make her clean after the killing, but these did not help. She could not forget that she had killed a man with her war club. Remembering was nearly driving her crazy. She could not think of anything else. She could not sleep at night. She could not chat with the other girls and women as they went about their daily work.

One day the Indian girl was wandering about, trying to forget. She heard a voice coming from a small adobe church. It was the voice of a white man speaking in the Pima language. The girl stood outside the little church, listening.

The voice was telling about a great God who loved everyone. His love was so great that he could forgive anyone who was sorry for doing wrong. God's love was so great that he gave sinners a chance to start fresh. They could leave their sins behind. They could be happy again, loving God and trying to live in his good way.

The Indian girl dared not believe this could be true, but she wanted to hear more about such a God. She wished she could believe. She knew where the white man, Dr. Charles Cook, lived. Finally she decided to go to his adobe house. She would ask him to tell her more about this God who loved and forgave.

As Dr. Cook talked, the girl wanted to believe. It would be so good to feel clean and happy again, cleaner and happier than ever before. She felt sure, however, that this wonderful forgiveness must be for little mistakes. It could not be for a big sin that kept a girl awake nights and drove her crazy remembering. She must find out by telling the missionary what a terrible thing she had done.

"I killed a man," the Pima girl told Dr. Cook. "Could God forgive me too after what I've done?"

"God forgives anything," said Dr. Cook. "He forgives if we are truly sorry, and if we forgive those who have wronged us."

So a new life came to the Indian girl as she knelt beside Dr. Cook on the hard adobe floor. She began to learn the ways of Christian love. She learned that Christians try to love everyone, even their enemies who have harmed them. As she grew in that love, the Pima girl helped others of her tribe find the God who had given her peace and joy.

When she was an old woman, someone asked her, "What was the greatest thing that happened to you in your long life?"

Her wrinkled face crinkled into a beautiful smile as she answered, "The greatest and most wonderful thing that ever happened to me was God's forgiveness."

(Source: *Indian Highways,* the bimonthly bulletin of the Cook Christian Training School of Phoenix, Arizona.)

A Boy and a Bee

A small boy named Albert sat on a stool watching his father take the honeycomb from the beehives. He was big enough to know that honey tasted good, but he was too small to know the difference between a butterfly and a bee. Any pretty thing that flew about with whirring wings was fun to watch, or fun to have for a pet.

The father was so busy with his work that he did not notice Albert moving his stool nearer and nearer to the hives. Taking out the honeycombs was ticklish work. It needed every bit of the father's attention. He did not notice the bees, angry at being disturbed, buzzing about the happy child who thought they were fun to watch.

A bee lighted on Albert's hand. That was still more fun. The boy was delighted to find that the pretty thing was so friendly.

Then suddenly, he found that the bee was not friendly after all. The poor bee felt that his world had turned topsy-turvy. There is only one thing for bees to do when they are disturbed. Naturally, the bee stung what was closest to him, the little boy's hand.

Naturally, too, Albert did what any small boy would do when stung by a bee. He screamed, and he screamed. The whole family came running to rescue him. One person picked him up to comfort him. Another scolded the father for letting Albert sit so near the hives. Everyone fluttered about the child, talking and making little comforting sounds. Albert was, for a few minutes at least, the most important person in the family, perhaps the most important person in the village.

There were plenty more tears where the first ones came from, so Albert cried and screamed and sobbed. The more fuss he made, the more he was petted. Everyone tried to think of a way to make him happy again.

Then Albert noticed something. He was crying just as hard as ever, with the tears streaming all over his face, but the bee sting was not really hurting any more. He knew it was time to stop his fussing. But he knew also that as soon as he stopped crying, people would stop comforting him and entertaining him and doing new and interesting things to make him happy. It was fun to be the center of attention. So Albert kept on crying.

Even though he was a small boy, however, Albert had a conscience that bothered him. When he finally did decide to stop crying, he was so ashamed of himself that he was unhappy for the rest of the day.

Now that he is more than eighty years old and very famous, Albert Schweitzer remembers how ashamed he was that day of making a fuss just to keep attention centered on himself. In a long life he has met great hardships and he has received great honors. He remains very calm about anything that happens to him. He takes what comes to him without trying to be the center of praise or of sympathy.

As an old man, Albert Schweitzer said that he never forgot what he learned the day he cried for attention long after the bee sting had stopped hurting. He says this memory has taught him, all his life, not to make too much of anything that happens to him.

(Source: *Memoirs of Childhood and Youth* by Albert Schweitzer, Macmillan Company, 1949.)

The Boy Who Mixed His Flags

It was a strange thing to find at midnight on a hillside in wartime—a boy curled in the shelter of a haystack. He was not more than five years old, far too young to be alone at night in the Shenandoah Valley, torn by the War between the States.

"What's this?" The Confederate officer stooped over the child. Rubbing sleepy eyes, the boy sat up and stared.

"Why is he here?" The officer turned to his young sergeant.

"That was his home!" The sergeant pointed at a heap of charred timbers which had been a house till yesterday's battle.

"His family?" asked the officer. The sergeant shook his head. Remembering how the bullets howled about the old farmhouse a few hours ago, the officer did not need ask more. Sadly he looked down at the waking child.

The boy felt it was time to make a friendly move. He smiled drowsily. Then he reached in his pocket and pulled out a bit of colored silk that he obviously thought was a treasure.

"See the flag!" he said. "Father gave it to me for the Fourth of July!"

It was the Union flag, not a pleasant sight to Confederate soldiers. But the officer gently lifted the boy to his shoulder.

"The little fellow does not know one flag from another. They are all beautiful to him." He turned to his sergeant and said slowly, "How I wish that *I* did not know one flag from another! How I wish that all flags were beautiful to me!"

Up the hill marched the officer, carrying the boy on his gray· uniformed shoulder. "We have made this child an orphan! We must take care of him!"

Suddenly there was a low shout from the surrounding darkness, then the glare of haystacks lighted by a dozen Yankee matches. On every side was the glint of Yankee guns, the blue of shabby Yankee uniforms. The Confederate soldiers knew that the volley from enemy guns would finish them before they could load their own muskets.

Just one of all that group on the hillside was not afraid. The sudden blaze, the many uniforms, the gleaming guns, excited the little boy on the Confederate officer's shoulder. He felt he should join in the celebration.

Out of his pocket he whipped the tiny bit of silk, the Stars and Stripes. "Hurrah! Hurrah for the Fourth of July!"

Fumbling at their muskets, the Confederate soldiers waited for the volley that did not come. In the light from the burning haystacks, they could see the Union soldiers salute the little scrap of red, white, and blue silk. They could see the men in blue drop quietly back into the darkness from which they had sprung.

"Saved!" said the Confederate officer. "Saved by a boy who thinks that all flags are beautiful to all people!"

(Source: The outline of this incident was found handwritten on a piece of yellowed paper tucked in an old book in an old attic. There is no way of knowing whether it is fact, legend, or fiction.)

On the Roof of the World

The homeland of Yoseb Gergan was the Roof of the World—Tibet. In Yoseb's boyhood, almost a century ago, Tibetans stayed in their rugged mountains and kept the rest of the world outside. Only traders traveled the long, high trails that wound through mountains to India or China. Their mule caravans carried yak wool and yak tails from Tibet. They brought back tea which Tibetans love to drink churned with yak butter.

There was no trading in ideas. Tibetans wanted nothing of the outside world's inventions, books, science, war, or religion. They were satisfied with their own Lamaism, a mixture of Buddhist beliefs and ancient Tibetan superstitions and rituals. They liked their own simple and peaceful way of life. They did not trust strangers.

Yoseb's father had fled from Tibet. The country was not safe for him because he had been accused of taking part in a murder. He had fled into the province of Ladak in Kashmir, just beyond the Tibetan border.

Ladak, once part of Tibet, was like his homeland. It had high mountains with deep snow in winter and alpine flowers watered by the mist and rain of summer, plateaus for barley fields, rushing streams in the valleys, long-haired yaks, and small houses of stone cemented with mud. The people of Ladak seemed like Tibetans, not like strangers whom Tibetans feared.

It was here, just over the border from Tibet, that Yoseb Gergan was born. It was here, as a boy, that he sat on the floor of the stone house day after day listening as his father taught the Tibetan language to the two missionaries from distant Moravia. There was so little excitement in Yoseb's world that he loved to hear their story over and over.

"Why did you come here?" he used to ask them.

"Back in Moravia, in Central Europe, we heard what religious people Tibetans are," they would say. "We heard of their prayer wheels, their prayer flags, their ritual dances, their fears of demons and evil spirits. We wanted to help them understand the true God."

Yoseb nodded. On the Ladak side of the border, he had seen the red-robed Tibetan monks whirling their prayer wheels, believing that every turn carried prayers toward Buddha. He had seen poles covered with flags on which prayers were written for people who believed that every breeze stirring the flags would blow the prayers toward Buddha. He had seen ritual dances to drive away demons. He had been warned many times, "Watch out! Do not anger the evil spirits!"

The Moravians told Yoseb, "We want to free Tibetans of fear. We want to tell them about God who loves us all, and about his son, Jesus, who came to bring us life."

Then the boy would listen, wide-eyed, to their tales of sailing stormy seas, traveling on foot and muleback across India and up mountain trails to Kashmir on Tibet's border.

"Then we could go no further," they would say. "The Tibetans believed their Lamaism was the only true faith. They did not want to hear about our religion. They would not let us enter their country."

"Then you met my father?" Yoseb liked this part best.

"Yes. He had recently come from Tibet and knew the language well. He agreed to teach it to us. Now, as you know, we work every day with him translating our Holy Bible into Tibetan."

Yoseb wondered about many things. One day he asked another question. "Who will read the Bible when it is written in our language? Only a few of us in Ladak speak Tibetan. You cannot carry the Book into Tibet to tell about it."

"You are a good thinker. We will try to explain," said one of the men. "We know we cannot go ourselves to carry the Bible. But we trust God. Our job is to make the best possible Tibetan translation. We believe God will find a way to use it."

Such talk gave Yoseb plenty to think about as he sat on the floor listening to his father and the missionaries. Sometimes they spent hours finding the right word. Other times they wrote pages in a day.

Yoseb heard them translating the Gospels, the stories of a man named Jesus who helped people and loved them and taught them how to get along together. This Jesus seemed to be following the eightfold path of goodness taught by Buddha: right beliefs, right resolves, right speech, right conduct, right ways of earning a living, right effort, right thinking, right concentration. Jesus added a ninth path—right loving. He was good in a way that was exciting and charming. He was never afraid. He seemed more interesting and friendly than the images of Buddha that Yoseb saw so often.

To Yoseb's father, translating the Bible was interesting work, nothing more. He still believed the Dalai Lama was the living

Buddha who should rule all Tibetans, even those who lived across the border in Ladak. He believed that the red-robed monks taught the only true faith. He liked the Moravian missionaries as friends. Let them have their own faith. He would keep his.

To Yoseb, however, the words being translated meant a new religion worth knowing. So he sat on the floor beside the translators, listening and thinking.

When Yoseb was old enough to read what had been written, he found the Gospels better for him than Lamaism. He was glad to learn that he could talk directly to God without needing a prayer flag to flutter his prayers heavenward. It was good to know that God came to earth in his friendly son, Jesus, who lives forever. That was better than one Dalai Lama after another living in the Lhasa Palace of the thousand rooms roofed by gold.

So Yoseb declared his faith in the loving God of Jesus Christ. He was the first Tibetan to believe the message of the two Moravian missionaries. They were proud of him.

"You must go to school more," they told him. "Our first Tibetan Christian must have a good education. There is great work for you to do."

So Yoseb went to a mission school in Srinagar, the capital of Kashmir. When he finished, he could have chosen among many good jobs with good wages. There were few young men in Kashmir with his character, his pleasant ways, and his learning. He had only one plan in life, however.

"I found Christ through reading the Bible," he said. "Now I want to give the Bible to the people of Tibet. I must finish the work started by my father and his friends."

For thirty-five years Yoseb Gergan worked with missionary translators to put the entire Bible into his language. As he worked, he wondered when any strangers would be allowed to go into his homeland to teach and preach. But he remembered how the Moravian friends of his boyhood believed that God would find a way.

Finally the entire Bible was translated into the language of Tibet. There was a heavy pile of precious pages carefully written in the Tibetan characters, which would look as strange to us as our printing would look to Tibetans.

The manuscript was then sent across the seas to be published in London by the British and Foreign Bible Society. But the Bible manuscript went to London at the wrong time. It was 1939. World War II was just beginning, and there was no chance of casting the Tibetan type. Worse than that, the manuscript was in danger when London was bombed. It was taken to Yorkshire in north central England to be hidden in the vault of Ripon Cathedral.

Far away in Ladak, Yoseb Gergan wondered what was happening to the Book to which he had given his life. When war ended in 1945, he wrote to the Bible Society in London, "Is the Bible manuscript safe? When will it be printed? When will my people of Tibet have the Bible in their own language?"

"The War has made it difficult to print the Tibetan Bible here in London," came the answer. "It must be printed by the Bible Society in Lahore."

So back across the ocean went the Bible manuscript to Lahore, a city southeast of Ladak, fifty-two days away by mule. But the Bible Society in Lahore had no type with characters of Tibetan script and no way of making such type. There seemed to be only one way to print the Bible. It must be written again by hand on paper treated by chemicals in such a way that it could be used as transfers. It must be written by a careful scholar who knew the Bible and the Tibetan language well.

In all the world there was just one such person! Yoseb Gergan had thought his life's work was done when he had completed the translation six years before. Now as an old man he began the long task of copying by hand the Book that had been the most important thing in his life ever since he sat on the floor as a boy and listened.

Knowing the work was long and his time short, he copied day and night with little rest. He found three helpers, Tibetan Christians who wrote the script well. Like him, they worked constantly with only short rests. One of these men, named Gapel, was later the hero of exciting journeys that made the printing of the Bible possible.

When Yoseb Gergan grew too frail, doctors tried to help him. They said, "He may live five days or five months. There is a fire burning within him that is keeping him alive."

In August, 1946, he finished the copying of the Bible onto the chemically treated sheets of paper. His Book was ready for the printing presses again. Only five days after he copied those last words the tired old man died. He was content. He had faith that God would use the work he had undertaken because as a little boy he used to sit on the floor listening.

God did use his work. Even though missionaries or colporteurs were not welcomed in Yoseb Gergan's home "on the roof of the world," traders were welcomed. Some of these traders were Christians who were glad to carry a few Tibetan Bibles, or parts of Bibles, with the goods they carried to sell.

Then, troubles in Tibet made many Tibetans flee across the borders into Nepal and North India. As refugees in a strange land some of them were happy when representatives of the Bible Society of India and Ceylon gave them books in their own language—parts of the Bible translation on which Yoseb Gergan had spent his life.

(Source: *The Story of the Tibetan Bible* by Canon Chandu Ray, published by British and Foreign Bible Society in Canada, 1958.)

IV

Folk Tales of Yesterday

Why the Thumb Stands Alone
(A Folk Tale of the Philippines)

As you know, every land has its "just so stories" to explain why things are as they are. Before there were books of science, people used these stories when children asked, "Why?"

Here is one from the Philippines, told by fathers and mothers when children looked at their own ten fingers and asked, "Why do our thumbs stand alone? Why do the four fingers pull away from the thumb?"

Long, long ago, so runs the tale, the five fingers on our hands were alike. They stood together. In those olden times the thumb was not lonely.

One day Little Finger was hungry. "Give me some food, please," he begged the finger next to him.

"I am hungry too, Little Finger," said Fourth Finger. "I do not know where to get food for you, nor even food for myself. What shall we do, Middle Finger?"

"I am hungry too, but I am not worried," said Middle Finger. "Heaven is kind. Heaven will send us food before we starve."

"But what if Heaven should not send us food?" asked Pointing Finger who was just as hungry as Little Finger, Fourth Finger, and Middle Finger. "What would happen then?"

The three fingers could not answer. They just looked at Pointing Finger and said nothing, because they knew of nothing to say.

Thumb had something to say. From his position close to Pointing Finger, he answered, "If Heaven does not feed us, we must steal food!"

"Steal?" gasped Pointing Finger.

"Steal?" cried Middle Finger.

"Steal?" asked Fourth Finger.

"Steal?"echoed Little Finger.

Then all together those four fingers said, "Never! Never! Never!" And they drew themselves as far from Brother Thumb as they could, murmuring, "We are hungry, but we would not steal food! Never! Never! Never!"

Thumb tried to explain why it would be all right to steal if they really needed something. "We would not be doing it out of mischief, or meanness, or greediness. We would be taking something we really needed. I don't see why that would be so terrible"

The four good and honest brothers kept pulling farther and farther away from Thumb. "Never! Never! Never!" They pulled so hard that they stretched the skin that fastened them to Thumb. They would have nothing to do with this tempting one who was telling them to do what they knew was wrong.

Ever since that day, so goes the folk tale, the fingers have kept as far as possible from their tempter. Ever since that day, Thumb has stood alone.

(Source: *Filipino Popular Tales* of the Memoirs of the American Folk Lore Society.)

The Discontented Camanchile Tree
(A Folk Tale of the Philippines)

Once upon a time a strong and beautiful camanchile tree grew in a little village beside the South China Sea. Because she had plenty of sun and air, the tree's branches were strong, her leaves were dark green, and her shape was evenly rounded. The children loved to play in her shade. The little tree was healthy and useful. She should have been perfectly happy. But she was sad.

The camanchile tree was sad because she had no blossoms, such as made the bougainvillaea vine or the flame tree bright and gay. She heard travelers as well as the villagers stop to admire the beauty of the flowering trees and vines. But nobody even looked up to say "thank you" when resting under the welcome shade of the camanchile tree.

One day the camanchile looked enviously at the golden blossoms of the passion vine growing on the ground below her. "How I wish I had lovely flowers like yours! Everyone praises you! Nobody notices me!"

Now it happened that the low-growing passion vine wanted nothing more than to move up higher in the world. She saw her chance to climb up where she could look out over the village and the South China Sea.

"You could be beautiful too," the passion vine told the unhappy camanchile tree.

"Me? Beautiful? How?"

"I will cover you with my flowers," offered Passion Vine.

It seemed a good idea. Camanchile invited the vine to grow all over it, from its lowest branches to its shapely crown. Camanchile was very happy. She loved to have the cheeping sunbirds with their long curved beaks suck nectar from the blossoms. She waved her branches in pride when children or grownups stopped to admire the golden flowers. Camanchile began to think that the flowers were her own.

As the months passed, however, Camanchile was not as full of joy and vigor. She found herself growing weaker with every golden sunset. Her leaves were pale instead of deep green. She longed for sunshine such as she used to know. She gasped for the air that used to blow about her so freely. She found herself com-

101

pletely covered by Passion Vine who had never grown so lush and strong when she crept along the shady ground.

"Let me breathe!" begged Camanchile. "You are smothering me!"

The vine only laughed and kept growing. "You invited me," she said. "You were not satisfied to be a tree without flowers. You wanted everyone to admire you for your blossoms. Why aren't you happy now that you are covered with flowers?"

"I have changed my mind," gasped Camanchile. "Leave me. Give me another chance. I'll never ask to be anything but a plain camanchile tree growing strong and green and shapely."

Passion Vine laughed again and sent out new shoots to smother the foolish camanchile tree even more completely.

(Source: *Filipino Popular Tales* of the Memoirs of the American Folk-Lore Society.)

The Ten-Dinar Bath
(A Persian Folk Tale)

One day **Mullah** Nasr-ed-Din went to the public bath of a big Persian city. In his own village everyone knew and honored him, even though they sometimes laughed at him and often laughed with him. In the big city, however, there were many persons who had never heard of a village teacher-priest named Mullah Nasr-ed-Din.

The man in charge of the public bath was one of these. He paid no attention to the shabby old man whose long, dark coat smelled like a donkey's saddle. Mullah Nasr-ed-Don stood around expecting someone to wait on him. The bath attendants, however, were all busy with men who looked more important than the old man from the country.

102

Nobody took the Mullah's clothes to put on a shelf for safe-keeping. Nobody led him to a warmed bench to sit for his bath. No attendant came to pour warm water over him. Nobody gave him soap. The attendants were all busy with the important customers.

Without help from anyone, the Mullah had to find a place for his clothes. He had to dip water and pour it over himself. He could find no soap. Nobody talked with him as he sat to enjoy the warm steam of the bath. While the bath attendants were rubbing the other bathers with big clean towels, Mullah Nasr-ed-Din had to dry himself with a damp towel someone had thrown in a corner.

Finally the Mullah was ready to leave. Then the bath attendant noticed him for the first time. There was a fee for a bath no matter how little help the customer received. The man was at the door with his hand open.

The Mullah hesitated while he did some of his quickest thinking. How could he teach the workers at the bath the lesson they needed to learn? As usual, his plan came quickly. Mullah Nasr-ed-Din opened his money bag, took out ten shining dinars, and dropped into the hand of the manager of the bath.

The man was so surprised that he nearly dropped the money. What a mistake he had made in judging this shabby old Mullah from the country! Who would have guessed that such a person would have paid ten times the usual fee? What might he have paid if he had been honored and flattered by the bath attendants? Before the Mullah was two steps outside the door, he could hear the buzz of excitment and wonder as the news of the ten-dinar fee spread.

The following week, Mullah Nasr-ed-Din went back to the same public bath. This time he was met at the door by bowing attendants. They were so eager to help their important customer that they got in each other's way. They folded his coarse clothes and laid them carefully away. They handled them as though they

103

were made of brocaded silk instead of homespun wool that smelled like a donkey's saddle.

The attendants led the Mullah to the warmest bench in the vaulted, steam-filled room. They poured hot water over him till he felt he was turning into a flowing river. They rubbed their sweetest scented soap on him. They chatted with him and crowded around to laugh at his jokes as he relaxed in the steaming room. They patted him with large clean towels till his body tingled. They helped him into his clothes again, a different man bringing each garment. And of course they gathered expectantly at the door when he was ready to leave.

Again the chief of the bath stood at the door with open hand. There was a hush as the Mullah stood beside him with great dignity and reached into his money bag. As one man, the attendants leaned forward and watched him drop one lonely dinar into the outstretched hand.

"Why?" came the chorus of surprised bath attendants.

"Why?" repeated the man in charge of the bath. "Why did you pay ten dinars last week when you had no help—and only one dinar this time when we gave you every attention? We did so much for you that the other men in the bath were grumbling that we neglected them. Why did you treat us that way?"

"Oh," explained the Mullah as he tucked his money bag inside his wide cotton belt. "This dinar pays for last week's bath. The ten dinars I gave you last week were for today's bath."

Climbing on the back of his waiting donkey, Mullah Nasr-ed-Din turned and grinned at the men who were standing with their mouths open, gazing after him. He wondered if they had learned their lesson.

(Heard in Iran from students who practiced their English on me by translating from a Persian book of folk tales.)

The Spiders' Christmas Eve
(A Legend of the Black Forest)

"Poor spiders!" Conrad watched a little gray spider slide out the door, pushed by his mother's busy broom. It hunted for a safe spot under the door step.

"Poor *me*, I'd say!" Conrad's mother jumped on a high stool to sweep a cobweb that was dangling from a high rafter. "Christmas Eve is only a few hours away, the house must be perfectly clean by then. And I find spiders' webs in the corners! Here's another spider! Out he goes!"

"Poor spiders!" Conrad watched a little black spider skid out the door. "It's because it is almost Christmas Eve that I'm sorry for the spiders!"

"Why?" Conrad's mother leaned on her broom. Her son did say the strangest things!

"At midnight the animals will come into the house to admire the Christmas tree," said Conrad. "But the poor little spiders will be huddled under the stone door step, too frightened to come back in the house. They *never* see the Christmas tree, because the house is always so clean for Christmas."

"That is true," agreed Conrad's mother.

"I think the spiders would like our Christmas tree just as much as the bigger animals do," said Conrad.

"Well, do not lie awake worrying about spiders," Conrad's mother kissed his troubled face. "They do not know what they are missing. You see, no good housewife in the Black Forest has ever left a single spider in her house on Christmas Eve."

Conrad did lie awake to worry about spiders, however. He listened to the little carved clock on the wall, made by his father who was the best clockmaker in the whole Black Forest. He heard it strike eight. He heard it strike nine.

Then suddenly, Conrad thought of a way to stop worrying.

He slipped out of his snug bed and knelt on the cold floor beside it.

"Dear God," prayed Conrad. "I think you are sorry for the spiders, too. Let them be happy on Christmas Eve, just like the other animals."

Then Conrad snuggled comfortably under his warm blankets. Why hadn't he remembered before that God loved little creeping things?

Conrad did not hear the clock strike ten—nor eleven. He slept through the first strokes of twelve.

Then he sat straight up in bed. There were other sounds mixed with the striking of the clock. There were soft footsteps in the corner where the Christmas tree stood. There were familiar voices that could speak words on just this one night of the whole year.

"It is even better than last year's tree!" said a barking voice.

"See how it shines!" said a purring voice.

"It smells of the woods and hills!" said a mooing voice.

"I am glad I was chosen to haul it from the forest!" said a neighing voice.

"I could roost in its green branches!" said a crowing voice.

All of this did not surprise Conrad. He knew, as every child of the Black Forest knew, that at midnight of Christmas Eve every animal that had served its family faithfully all the year could come into the house to admire the Christmas tree.

But what happened next was a surprise to Conrad.

As the animals quietly slipped from the house, there came the sound of many feet, such tiny feet that only ears like Conrad's could have heard them. The little feet swarmed over the door sill. They crossed to the corner where the Christmas tree stood. Then there was a faint rustling in the branches of the tree.

Conrad slid out of bed. He tiptoed to the tree.

"God *does* love little creeping things!" he whispered. "The spiders have come to see the tree!"

But what were they doing? They would ruin the beautiful tree that his father and mother had trimmed so carefully!

In and out, up and down among the branches hurried the spiders—hundreds of them. They must be all the spiders swept from every house in the whole Black Forest on the day before Christmas. Wherever they went, they left fragile webs trailing behind them. When the tree was festooned from top to bottom with gray, lacy webs, the spiders disappeared as quickly as they had come.

"The clean beautiful tree is spoiled," thought Conrad. "It is all my fault! I should never have prayed that the spiders might be happy with the big animals on Christmas Eve! What shall I do now? I can never wipe off all those webs!"

Just then a bright light sparkled and danced through the room, making it brighter than at sunny noon. Conrad had heard that the Christ Child visited the Christmas trees on Christmas Eve at the hour when the animals could speak. But Conrad had never been awake to see the light before. It shone on the tree, on the feathery maze of the spiders' webs. It turned them to silver and to gold. It was the most beautiful tree that had ever brightened a home in the whole Black Forest.

Conrad tiptoed back to bed. He did not hear another sound till sunlight was filling the room. Then he remembered what had happened in the night. He rushed to the tree to see if it was true.

There stood the most beautiful Christmas tree in the world, covered from top to bottom with slender festoons of silver and delicate webs of gold. The spiders and the Christ Child had left a bright and glistening "thank you" for the boy who had felt sorry for the insects other people despised, and who loved spiders enough to pray for them.

The story of the gold and silver hangings on Conrad's tree spread through the Black Forest. Ever after that, on the day before Christmas, the good housewives scrubbed and polished till their houses shone. But they did not sweep spiders out into the cold.

Ever after that, so runs the old legend, Christmas trees have been trimmed with glistening streamers of silver and of gold. If you do not believe this story, look at your own Christmas tree, and see for yourself!

(Note: If you find another version that differs from this, the other is probably more authentic. This story is enlarged from a brief reference in a magazine article on Christmas customs and legends.)

V

The Bible in Today's World

What We Owe Mary Jones

Mary Jones did not go to school nor learn to read until she was ten years old. There was no Bible in her home until she was sixteen. But, because of Mary Jones, a weaver's child who was born in Wales in 1788, the Bible has been given to millions of persons in their own language.

Mary's parents could not read, but her father was a good story-teller. Mary's favorite stories were the ones he told about Joseph, Moses, David, Jesus, Paul, and other Bible heroes. He had learned them from hearing the Bible read in church in their own Welsh language.

Mary had two wishes: "I wish I could read! I wish we had a Bible in our house!"

Her father used to tell her, "Only rich people can afford to own Bibles."

When Mary was ten years old her first wish came true. A school was started two miles from where she lived. Walking four miles over rugged hills each school day did not bother Mary. She learned to read quickly.

A well-to-do farmer who lived nearby owned a Welsh Bible. His wife invited Mary to come to her house to read it. The more she read, the more Mary wanted a Bible of her own.

By raising hens, ten-year-old Mary Jones began to earn and save money to buy a Bible. Half-penny by half-penny her savings box grew heavier. When she was sixteen, she had saved enough to buy a Welsh Bible. But there was no bookstore in her village!

Someone told Mary, "Reverend Thomas Charles of the church in Bala, over the hills, has some Bibles to sell. But that is twenty-five miles away—and the trails are steep!"

To a girl who had worked six years to save money for a Bible, a hike of twenty-five miles to buy it and twenty-five miles to bring it home was not too much. Mary Jones walked barefoot, carrying her only pair of shoes to save them. Just outside Bala she sat down and put them on. She must be properly dressed when she met Mr. Charles and asked to buy a Bible.

He had bad news for her. "I have only three Welsh Bibles left! They are all promised to others! I do not know when I can get more!"

Brave Mary did what any tired and disappointed girl would do. She cried. And Mr. Charles did what any kind-hearted minister would do. He said, "Mary Jones, I'll find you a Welsh Bible somehow!"

One of the three who had ordered Welsh Bibles agreed to wait. So Mary had her Bible. Of course Mr. Charles arranged for Mary's food and lodging before she started over the hills for home, carrying her hard-won Bible.

Mr. Charles could not stop thinking about Mary. He knew she was only one of many Welsh people who wanted Bibles but could not afford such expensive books or did not know where to buy them.

"There ought to be enough Welsh Bibles for every family in Wales," thought Mr. Charles. "The price should be small, so anyone could buy. The Bibles should be sold in the villages so people would not have to travel miles of mountain trails to find them. Not everyone is as brave and persistent as Mary Jones. I must do something to help them have Bibles!"

Mr. Charles went from Bala to London, a long journey in those days, to share his problem with the Religious Tract Society. Because of his visit, the British and Foreign Bible Society was founded in London in 1804 "to encourage the wider circulation of the Holy Scriptures without note or comment."

Now there are Bible Societies all over the world, including the American Bible Society which began work in 1816. These many Bible Societies work together as the United Bible Society. They translate the Bible into new languages. They print it so that it can be bought cheaply. They work with churches and missionaries. They have Bible stores all over the world, and Bible salesmen or colporteurs who go into villages or into city streets carrying the Bible to people who may never have seen it before.

This all happened because a weaver's daughter in Wales wanted a Bible enough to work for it.

(Sources: Publications of the Bible Societies, especially "The Story of Mary Jones" a leaflet by Doris W. Street published by the British and Foreign Bible Society.)

The Second-Class Rascal

In Peh-Kong, a Chinese village of low brick houses, lived an unhappy family. The father, Chan, was known to everyone as "the Second-Class Rascal" of Peh-Kong. He was cruel to his wife, to his children, and to his neighbors. He was dishonest in his business, selling spoiled fish for the price of fresh.

Chan hated everyone. Most of all he was filled with jealous hatred for Ping who was known as "the First-Class Rascal" of Peh-Kong. In a quarrel, Chan killed Ping and took his place as "First-Class Rascal." Now everyone feared Chan—not only in his village but in all the neighboring villages as well. Women would buy his spoiled fish rather than risk his anger if they refused. In all Taiwan there was no sadder family than the neglected and abused wife and children of Chan.

111

One evening a miracle happened. A blue car that was something like a truck and something like a station wagon jounced over the rough roads between the shining wet rice fields. It was marked with big Chinese characters that meant Bible Society. Its passengers, including Pastor Lai, went from house to house inviting people to meet near the car.

So little usually happened in Peh-Kong that everyone was glad to come. Even Chan joined the crowd. So did his children, standing as far as possible from him. Pastor Lai and his helpers set up a big white screen and started a battery buzzing inside the car.

As soon as it was dark, pictures flashed on the screen. The villagers saw pictures of Jesus taking little children in his lap, preaching to crowds, healing cripples and crazy folks, talking to friends who loved him, and dying on a cross to save people from their sins.

Pastor Lai explained, "Jesus still lives. He still loves everyone. He leads us to a kind God who forgives our sins." Pastor Lai held up five paper-covered books. Anyone who knew Chinese characters could sound out their names—Matthew, Mark, Luke, John, the Acts.

"These books tell about Jesus," said Pastor Lai. "There are enough books for all of you. Just sign your name. You can pay three cents for the five books if you have the money."

"Look!" The children of Chan nudged each other. "Our father is walking up front! He is signing his name! He is counting out the three cents! He is taking the books!"

In the next few days the children of Chan watched him reading the little books. Sometimes he would read aloud to his wife and children. Then Chan would sigh, lay down his books, pick up his fish vendor's basket, and go out to his work. While he was at his selling, he was still "the First-Class Rascal"—lying about his spoiled fish and shouting at women who tried not to buy from him.

Watching him, one of his children dared ask, "You do not believe what you read in the little books?"

"The books are true for some—but not for me," Chan answered. "Evil rules me. Nothing can save me."

Then one day when Chan was reading the little books, he gave a shout of joy. "Listen to this!" His wife and children squatted on the hard ground beside his bench to listen.

"The books tell of a thing called prayer," said Chan. "It is not the prayer we have known—laying an offering in the wayside shrine. This prayer is talking with God. God helps people who pray to him. Jesus taught his friends to pray, like this . . ."

Then Chan read the prayer that begins "Our Father." When he came to the words, "Deliver us from evil," he read them again and again.

"What do you think of that?" he asked. " 'Deliver us from evil.' I thought nothing could save me from the evil ways of my life. But these little books tell me that God will help me if I ask him to deliver me from evil. I want you all to pray with me."

God's forgiving love was stronger than the evil that held Chan in its clutches. Now in Peh-Kong there is a clean restaurant run by a kind and smiling man who was once "the First-Class Rascal." All the food is good, but his fish is best of all.

Chan's wife is happy in her clean home with a cheerful husband and plenty of rice for her family, and the children of Chan are the happiest boys and girls in all Taiwan. They like their home full of laughter, their clean school uniforms, their friendly neighbors. But, most of all, they are happy that their father is no longer "the Second-Class Rascal" nor "the First-Class Rascal" but a First-Class Christian.

(Source: This true story was told to me by Pastor P. T. Lai when I visited his office in the Bible House in Taichung, Taiwan.)

Owls and Shadows

Pedro had not been a Christian long. He had believed in ghosts and spirits more years than he had believed in one loving God. It was hard for Pedro to forget stories his neighbors told of evil spirits that lived in trees, in rocks, in flowing water. It was hard to remember always that he was a Christian now.

Pedro's mountainous part of the Philippine Islands was not touched when the Spaniards conquered the beautiful green islands in the sixteenth century and sent missionaries of the Roman Catholic Church. Nobody had climbed those high hills to teach a different faith than fear of ghosts and spirits till Protestant preachers came.

Pedro had gone to the new church. He had been baptized and learned to recite many verses from the Bible. He was glad to be a Christian--but sometimes he forgot.

The night of our story was a time he found himself thinking of ghosts and spirits, not thinking of the one God who loved him. It was the darkest of dark nights. Pedro was on an errand from his own mountain village to another mountain village a few miles away.

You who live among street lights, house lamps, and automobile headlights have little idea how dark the world can be where none of these lights are shining. There was no moon that night. The stars were behind the clouds. There was no brightness but the small flame of Pedro's lantern as he walked slowly, feeling his way along the trail.

Every frightful story he had ever heard popped into his mind. The soft hooting of the owl seemed eerie to him. The hoarse "gek-ko" of the big green lizards seemed like shrieks of wicked demons. The scratching of one tree limb upon another seemed like wails from another world. A big fruit bat swished close to him and made him jump.

114

Pedro would have turned about and run for home, but he had gone too far. It was as bad to turn back as to go on.

"I wish I had the charm I used to wear before I was baptized," thought Pedro. "That was supposed to keep away evil spirits. My new Christian religion has no charms."

Pedro stumbled on. He thought of the new faith that was supposed to make him strong and brave. He tried to pray, but he could not think of the right words. Pedro had been a Christian such a short time that he had not learned that God hears prayers that have no words.

Then Pedro tried reciting Bible verses. He remembered one about "the valley of the shadow of death." The valleys between these mountains were surely full of the shadow of death on such a night of noises and darkness. He would see how many words he could remember.

"The Lord is my shepherd," Pedro recited in a loud voice. He wondered what made that clump of tree ferns sway so hard.

"I shall not want. He maketh me to lie down in green pastures." He hoped that noise was a big lizard rustling off through the grass—not a ghost.

"He leadeth me beside the still waters. He restoreth my soul," recited Pedro. This was the time of night when poisonous snakes were about, but he would rather meet a snake than an evil spirit.

"He leadeth me in the paths of righteousness for his name's sake. Yea, though I walk through the valley of the shadow of death, I will fear no evil, for thou art with me." That *thou* meant God, didn't it? Did it mean that God was really with Pedro here on the dark mountain trail?

"Thy rod and thy staff they comfort me." It was good to think of God walking beside him, taking care of him.

"Thou preparest a table before me in the presence of mine enemies." Enemies? That would mean ghosts or spirits. No, not really! His new religion taught there were no ghosts nor spirits.

It must mean the *fear* of ghosts and spirits. Fear was Pedro's enemy.

"Surely goodness and mercy shall follow me all the days of my life: and I will dwell in the house of the Lord for ever."

Pedro walked with a lighter step. Suddenly he was not afraid. The psalm was like a prayer to him—like the prayer for which he had not been able to find words. It made him feel that God was with him.

Pedro looked at the clumps of trees and laughed. He knew wind, shadows, owls, and big green lizards for what they were. There was nothing on that trail at night more dangerous than he met without a thought when he ran along it in the daytime.

"The Lord is my shepherd," Pedro began again. He could not tell how many times he recited that psalm before he came near enough the neighboring village to see the glow of small red kerosene lamps in square, thatched houses on posts. But he could tell without a doubt that the psalm put courage into his heart and a spring into his walk.

(Source: This story is based on an item in *Christian World Facts* 1952, but I have met many a Pedro on Philippine trails.)

The Book from the Street

Kiku nearly stepped on the little book before she noticed it lying in the street of her small village in the hills of Japan. The book was dirty and crumpled. Others had been walking on it.

Like every Japanese schoolgirl, Kiku loved to read. Even a small and dirty book interested her. She stooped to pick it up. She walked toward home slowly, reading as she walked.

This little book was very different from her schoolbooks, or from the magazines she liked to buy when she had a few extra yens. She finished reading it before she spread her bed pad on the straw mats of the floor to sleep that night. She read parts of it over again the next day.

She thought of the little book when she heard her father and mother talking about a neighbor, Ayako-San.

"Poor Ayako-San!" sighed Kiku's mother. "She is lonely and sad ever since her husband died."

"She is looking everywhere for comfort," said Kiku's father. "She goes often to the Shinto shrine. She pays many yen for paper prayers at the shrine. She has been to the Buddhist priest also. Nothing he says helps her. She even made a pilgrimage to the sacred Temple city, but still she weeps and mourns."

"She should think of her children," said Kiku's mother. "She should think of making a happy home for them. There must be something to make her glad to live again."

Then Kiku had her idea. On her way to school that morning, Kiku stopped at the home of Ayako-San. As usual, she found the poor woman crying. Kiku held out the little book she had found in the street.

"Take it and read it," said Kiku. "I found it in the street where someone had dropped it. I read it. There is a wonderful story in it of a man who helps those who are sad and helpless. I thought of you. I think you will like the story."

Ayako-San bowed her thanks. Even a very sad Japanese lady would remember to be polite.

Kiku ran toward school. Ayako-San wiped her eyes on the gray sleeve of her kimono. Now she could see the Japanese characters of the little torn book. She would read a few words just to see what Kiku thought was so wonderful.

Ayako-San read one page—and another—and another. It was just what Kiku had said, the "wonderful story of a man who helps those who are sad and helpless." She turned to what was left of the cover page and found the book was named *St. Luke's Gospel.*

As Ayako-San read the little book again and again, she found much that she could understand and much that she could not understand. She wished there was someone to tell her, but nobody in that hill village knew. Nobody could answer Ayako-San's questions.

One day she walked down the rough trails to the market town to sell the eggs her few hens had laid. Right in the center of the busy market she saw a man talking to a crowd. She joined them to hear what he was saying. He was talking about the man of her little book! She recognized the Japanese name, Iesu Kirisuto. When the man finished talking there were still questions Ayako-San wanted to ask.

"Will you come to my village?" Ayako-San pointed toward the road leading into the hills. "Nobody there knows about Iesu Kirisuto. Will you come and tell us?"

Of course the answer was "yes" from the colporteur, the seller of Bibles.

In a few months there were enough Christians in that little village to make a church.

When they met there was none with a face more full of calm and peace than Ayako-San. And there was none more full of excitement than Kiku. She knew that the church of Iesu Kirisuto was bringing new joy into her village because she had stooped to pick up the little book in the street—and had read it—and had shared it.

(Source: *The Bible in Japan* by James C. F. Robertson, British and Foreign Bible Society.)

Woodpile and Pickle Jar

Many stories could be written about Korean women who showed great courage during the Korean War of 1950. Dong Hi Kim-Im was one of these brave Korean women. She used her courage, her brains, a woodpile, and a pickle jar to save the new Hankul translation of the Korean Bible.

The Korean Bible was printed in old script which only scholars could read easily. A new version in modern script was ready for the printing press. Dong Hi Kim-Im was the wife of Young Kim-Im, General Secretary of the Bible Society in Korea. He was responsible for the printing of the new Hankul translation on the press of the Bible House in Seoul.

When armies of North Korea swept into Seoul in 1950, one of the first places they destroyed was the Bible House. It was impossible for Young Kim-Im to save the building or the printing press, but he did save the new Hankul version of the Bible in its handwritten script. When he knew that the soldiers were near, he carried it home and hid it in a big cooking pot.

Several times the North Korean soldiers stormed up to his home to take him away as a prisoner. Always his wife came to the door and politely let them search the house for him. They never found him. Always after they were gone, Dong Hi Kim-Im would go to the woodpile in their yard. She would remove a few big sticks of wood.

"They have gone," she would whisper to her husband. "It is safe to come out now."

"Is the Bible manuscript safe?" he would ask.

"It is safe. They did not look in the pot."

"Safe once more, but perhaps not safe the next time," Young Kim-Im would answer.

Finally he thought of a safer place to hide it. He remembered friends who lived in a village a few miles from Seoul. These friends were loyal Christians, and brave.

"The Bible manuscript would be safe buried in their garden," Young Kim-Im said to his wife.

"How could we take it there?" she asked. "The streets are full of soldiers. They would search a package."

"I have been thinking about that," he said. "You can put it in a pickle jar and carry the jar on your head to our friends' home in the village. Then bury it in their garden."

Dong Hi Kim-Im looked at her husband, amazed. Could he mean what he said? "It would be very dangerous!" she said.

"It is dangerous to keep it here in the cooking pot," he answered.

Dong Hi Kim-Im stared at him. Was he serious? Did he really expect her to walk through the soldier-crowded streets carrying the precious manuscript in a pickle jar on her head?

"I could place pickles on top, so that the soldiers would see those if they looked inside," she said. "I could wrap the pickle jar in a bigger bundle with clothes and things. I could dress like a village woman who has been to market."

That is what she did. There were so many soldiers on the main road that she took a longer route to the village. For several miles nobody paid any attention to a country woman on her way home with a bundle on her head.

When she had nearly reached the village of her friends, a young Communist soldier stopped her. He searched her bundle. He saw the clothes and the ordinary pickle jar.

"What is in there?" he asked, though he supposed it was nothing but pickles.

"I am carrying pickled cucumbers," she said. The soldier did not bother to open the jar, so he never saw what was under the pickled cucumbers. He let her pass.

Dong Hi Kim-Im plodded wearily on till she reached her friends' home. They helped her dig a deep hole in the garden.

After they took out the pickled cucumbers, they buried the jar with the precious Hankul manuscript hidden safely inside. There it stayed until the Communist armies were driven north from Seoul.

Then it was Dong Hi Kim-Im who walked the miles back to her friends' village through a countryside where bandits and bands of armed men were roaming. She dug up the jar and found the Bible manuscript safe. Through the same dangerous roads she brought it back to her husband.

There were other adventures before it could be printed. But at last, in 1952, the Hankul Bible was printed, thanks to the brave woman who guarded it. Now many Koreans who cannot read the difficult letters of the old Korean Bible can read the Bible printed in modern new script.

(Source: The leaflet "Dong Hi Kim-Im" in the series *Doers of the Word* of the British and Foreign Bible Society.)

On the Barge Canal

Not all colporteurs sell their Bibles in faraway places like Taiwan or Japan. A small boy named Tom learned that when he was on his father's tugboat in New York Harbor years ago.

Tom was standing at the gunwale of the tug watching the many boats puffing and tooting. The tugboat was anchored while the barges it was to pull were being loaded.

Tom noticed a man rowing toward him. This was not a young man. He bent over the oars as though rowing was hard work.

"Who is he?" wondered Tom. "He's steering this way!"

When the old man pulled alongside, he did not board the tugboat. He simply handed Tom a book and told him a few things about it. Then he rowed away, leaving Tom with a new book, a Bible.

Tom read the Bible—and liked it. He liked the exciting stories in the Old Testament. He liked the outdoor poems in the book of Psalms. He liked the good news of the New Testament. This Book gave him new ideas that grew with him as he became a man in the rough life on the canal.

Now he is "Captain Tom" with a large tugboat of his own. With his crew he moves barges full of grain, oil, or other cargo through the barge canal that follows the Mohawk and Hudson Rivers between Buffalo and New York City.

Captain Tom also carries another cargo in his cabin. This cargo weighs little, but is worth much. The captain has not forgotten that he is a better and happier man because an old colporteur rowed out to his father's tugboat in New York Harbor when he was a boy. So Captain Tom has a supply of Bibles in his cabin. These were given, at his request, by the Syracuse office of the American Bible Society. This Society is glad to give the captain as many Bibles as he can distribute to persons who do not have them.

These men and boys of the ports along the barge canal are ready to accept a Bible from a man who is their own rugged sort of outdoor worker. They know that he has to take rough weather and strong currents. They know he can handle heavy anchor chains, climb ladders in wind and rain, throw ropes to men on barges, and manage his own cargo. They know his own crew respects and obeys him.

"If this Book is good for a regular guy like Captain Tom," these canallers say, "it's good for me."

Captain Tom has heard Erie Canal history that happened many years before he met his colporteur in New York Harbor. Way back in 1833 the Bible Society of Utica watched the streams of people moving west on the Erie Canal. In a single year as many as 175,000 people traveled the Erie Canal through Utica.

Most of these people were going west to settle in the new lands. As you know, "west" in those days meant Buffalo or beyond. This Erie Canal was the best route to the Great Lakes and the new lands that lay beyond them.

The Bible Society in Utica knew Bibles should go west with these immigrants. So its workers met the canalboats as they tied up in Utica. There were Bibles and New Testaments also for the crewmen and owners of canalboats.

So, when Captain Tom finds someone who needs one of the Bibles he carries in the cabin of his big tugboat, he knows he is part of a chain of people who have given Bibles on the canal. First, there was the Utica Bible Society before he was born— then the colporteur in New York Harbor when he was a boy— and now, Captain Tom himself.

(Source: "Assignment: The Bible on the Barge Canal" by Gerald E. Boyce in *Bible Society Record,* American Bible Society, November, 1958.)

Captain Fuchida

Captain Mitsue Fuchida was the captain of the Japanese bomber that led the attack on Pearl Harbor in December, 1941. He had learned to hate Americans long before he dropped bombs on Pearl Harbor, Hawaii. His hatred of Americans began when he lived for a short time in San Francisco, California. There he heard of the law which kept Japanese and other Asians from coming into the United States to work and become American citizens. He felt this law showed scorn of his own people. He hated a country that would treat Japanese that way.

So Captain Fuchida was glad when, as ace flyer in the Japanese air force, he was given the order to lead the squadron of 360 bombers in the Pearl Harbor attack. Here was his chance to get even with a country that had passed laws that seemed an insult to the Japanese people. He dropped the bombs with a feeling of revenge. He rejoiced as the bombs fell on Pearl Harbor from other planes. All through the war he was glad that his had been the chance to lead the first bombing.

It was after the war that Captain Fuchida met two people who changed his way of thinking.

The first was a Japanese man who had been in America while it was at war with Japan. Like many persons of Japanese ancestry, he was shut in a prisonlike camp. This happened, unfortunately, even to some persons of Japanese ancestry who were among our best American citizens.

While this Japanese friend was in the camp which was almost a prison, a young American girl came to the camp regularly to bring food, magazines, and other gifts to the Japanese.

"Why do you do this?" he asked her. "We are your enemies. Why do you treat us as friends?"

"My father and mother were Christian missionaries in Japan," she told him. "When war broke out between the United States and Japan, my parents were imprisoned, tortured, and killed by Japanese officers. Just before their death they wrote me, 'Always love the people of Japan!'"

"Why?" he asked.

She showed him her Bible. She explained its teaching of love to enemies.

Captain Fuchida listened to his friend's story of kindness by a Christian American girl to a man of the country whose officials had killed her own parents. It made him wonder.

Then Captain Fuchida met an American sergeant who was in Tokyo, Japan, soon after the war ended. His was the second story that changed Captain Fuchida's way of thinking.

"I was captured by the Japanese," the American sergeant told him. "They put me in prison and gave me a really hard time. I hated them bitterly. Then I found a Bible. I had never bothered to read a Bible when I was free, but in prison there was nothing else to do. So I read that Bible. Parts of it I read over many times. I thought about it. I even found myself praying about it.

"My bitterness and hatred melted away. I made up my mind that, if I was alive after the war, I would return to Japan and teach what I had found in that Bible—the love that forgives."

The stories of the forgiving girl and the forgiving sergeant made Captain Fuchida think. Could anything make him forgive his old enemies, the Americans? He decided to get a copy of the Book that taught that kind of love.

Reading the Bible, Captain Fuchida also learned the love that forgives. It was eleven years after he led the attack on Pearl Harbor that Captain Fuchida became a Christian. Now the biggest thing in his life is sharing his firm Christian faith of love and joy and forgiveness with his own people of Japan.

(Source: I heard the story from Japanese Christians while in Japan. See "The 'Lime' of Japan" by Clara Paine Otis in *Christian World Facts* 1957-58.)

Bimbo —Hero

Bimbo did not look like a hero. He did not seem a dog who could ever be a hero. He was little and black, with perky ears that always seemed to be listening and a sharp nose that always seemed to be sniffing.

Bimbo traveled the three thousand miles across Africa from Johannesburg in the Transvaal to Kano in Nigeria in the pilot's cockpit of a Super Constellation. He was a sleepy little puppy when he made that trip.

Bimbo grew to be as faithful a dog as ever guarded a master from interruption. The small black dog seemed to sense that his master must not be disturbed when he was at work. Of course Bimbo had no idea what the tall white man and his dark-skinned African friends were doing when they sat for hours at a table with books and paper and pencils. It did not matter to Bimbo that his master was hard at work translating the Bible into Hausa, the dialect of the Africans of that part of Nigeria.

Bimbo could understand only a few important words such as "Come," and "Sit down," and "Shake hands." He did not share his master's worries about finding just the right words in Hausa to give God's message.

Translating a Bible is a very difficult task. No English-speaking person could do it alone and make the words right to people whose native tongue was Hausa. It was necessary to go often to work in a little resthouse in the "bush," the wild country far from cities. There Bimbo's master could find African Christians to help him choose the right words for their Bible in their language. Bimbo always went with his master on these trips into the bush.

Bimbo took his work seriously. He must guard his master from everyone and from everything. If a goat strayed near, Bimbo would chase him away so fast that his master did not hear any bleating. If a donkey wandered toward the veranda of the resthouse, the little dog was at his heels before the donkey had time to bray. Chickens, pigs, anything that came that way met the same treatment.

If Bimbo closed his eyes, his ears and nose were still alert. The little black dog seemed to realize that his master and the African helpers were so intent on their work at the table that they did not know what was going on about them. It was Bimbo's job to watch.

One morning while the men were stooped over their books and papers in the resthouse in the bush, Bimbo suddenly saw and smelled something different from the goats and donkeys that ran away so easily when he nipped at them. Bimbo's good dog sense told him that this long black thing slithering through the grass toward his master was a bad enemy. This strange long creature had no heels to nip. Bimbo did not know where to attack it. But he knew enough to bark and bark and bark.

Bimbo's barks were so frantic that the busy men looked up. They saw a great hooded cobra. Its head was lifted in anger, waving from side to side. It was ready to strike. The men knew that the bite of a cobra is deadly.

Before they had time to do anything, the cobra took revenge on the small black animal that was challenging it. Into Bimbo's eyes, the cobra spat its poison. Then when everyone rushed to help poor Bimbo, the cobra sneaked away to hide.

The story has a happy ending. There was medicine to cure Bimbo's eyes. One of the African helpers, who knew the ways of cobras, found its hiding place and killed it.

When the Hausa translation is finished, part of the praise should go to the faithful little black dog whose bright eyes saw the dangerous cobra before it attacked.

(Source: *In Every Land,* the children's publication of the British and Foreign Bible Society.)